Herbert Maeder   The Mountains of Switzerland

The Mountains of Switzerland

The Adventure of the High Alps

Edited, with photographs and commentary,
by Herbert Maeder
with an Introduction by Dr Werner Kämpfen
and contributions by Professor
Georges Grosjean, and Dr Ricco Bianchi
Translated by Hendrik P. B. Betlem

Walker and Company New York

Contents

Werner Kämpfen

The Adventure of the High Alps

Anyone looking over books of photographs produced during the last few years usually overlooks (forgive the pun) the landscape illustrated: the air photograph is predominant, the view is taken from a point higher than could ever be reached on foot. A faithful view from the skies, it is nevertheless cold and impersonal, machine made.

I have nothing against aviation or air photography. Both have given us new perspectives and dimensions of the greatest value to the cartographer and the surveyor. They have given new scope to the painter and designer. The alpine world looks orderly from such heights, and modern man, accustomed to orderly abstractions, applauds what he sees, possibly because from these elevated heights it is impossible to distinguish individual objects such as masts and cables, architectural monstrosities and urban sprawl scattered haphazardly across the landscape. Has progress in air photography reduced mountains to a prosaic mediocrity and disrupted their relation to mankind? Mittelholzer's pictures still show the alpine huts, those of the cosmonauts simply give part of an atlas.

Herbert Maeder still follows the old, difficult tracks of individual man. His viewpoints are attained by climbing the hard way. That can be seen from his photographs: the camera is half-way to the summit or coming down from it. Even where no one is to be seen, his presence can be discerned. Here is the ridge which has just been climbed, this sérac or that cleft has just been scaled, and through the stark loneliness of the mountains a human spirit breathes. But the romanticism of the early alpine explorers is no part of modern mountaineering, any more than is the false pathos of the "mountain stream and edelweiss" type of book. The modern attitude to the mountains is objective and single-minded. Gaston Rébuffat calls the obelisk, titan or giant of Zermatt a "*merveilleux tas de pierres*", a wonderful heap of stones. Herbert Maeder, mountain climber by calling and photographer by profession, knows the right moment to exchange the ice-axe for the camera, just as later he takes up his objective pen. His chapter on "Becoming a Mountaineer" is an expression of this style, an undisguised song of praise to alpinism.

This book is called *The Mountains of Switzerland*—certainly a geographic but by no means a national or nationalist qualification. Herbert Maeder and his fellow contributors keep to their own mountains, because they have personally undertaken excursions to them: to the Eiger, to the Bernina, to the whole galaxy of the Swiss peaks, to study them to the last detail. Their knowledge is of the peaks they have climbed, but their enthusiasm—as can be sensed—is for all the mountains of the Alps, Austrian, Julian and Bavarian, the Dolomites, the Dauphiné and all the other parts. From most of the alpine summits, the mountaineer can see far beyond national frontiers, transcending the chauvinism on the ground below. Let us avoid degrading mountaineering feats by representing them merely as national achievements!

This book is published at a time when motoring interests are describing our Alps as the greatest obstacle in Europe, as an "awkward barrier", to be pierced by as many tunnels as possible or, better still, by one enormous tunnel starting in Basle and ending in Chiasso—underground through Switzerland and the Alps! There has been no lack of reaction to such one-sided worship of speed and the internal combustion engine. Rarely before in the history of alpinism has the number of visitors to the mountains increased so rapidly as in the last few years. Even the most hardened characters are now seeking in mountain trips to recover their lost equinamity. Younger people are flocking to the climbing schools. The challenge of the heights is exactly what the younger generation is seeking. Here there is no need for complicated technical equipment. The only requirements are a pair of mountaineering boots, healthy lungs, plenty of self-assurance, and above all a desire to achieve something. When the young climber finally stands on his peak and looks down to the plains stretching below him, where the cars emerge from the alpine tunnel, he is entitled to the feeling of quiet satisfaction which comes over him.

This is the train of thought which will come to the reader of this book. It is not something to be looked at superficially, nor to be hurried through. It requires frequent pauses, a well-considered stage during the mountain ascent. Only then will we be able to take in the mountaineer's experiences and sense the impression of the mountain scene, for which we have to thank author and publishers. For however easily the alpine explorer in the course of his own travels can experience the wonderful silences and the exhilaration of the heights, so much the more difficult is it to convey these impressions in words and pictures. This is indeed a task of the greatest difficulty. Here it has been nobly achieved.

Georges Grosjean

Man and Mountain through the Ages

Historical Note
on the Exploration and
Opening up of the
Swiss Alps

During the middle ages, educated people looked upon mountains with terror and avoided any close contact with them. Superstitious tales of spirits and monsters, as well as a deeply religious and overwhelming awe for the grandeur of creation, kept people away from them. But this was merely the reaction of educated circles in the lowlands. That this was the way they liked to express themselves in writing must not be taken to mean that the inhabitants of the alpine valleys of that period did not know their own mountains intimately. They moved around them with a self-assurance which can only astonish us today and to some extent can be surmised only with difficulty from what is now known about mountain conditions. Rope and ice-axe were unknown before the end of the eighteenth century. On the other hand, snow shoes, rough sleds, climbing irons and long sticks were described and illustrated during the sixteenth century, and even before that there are references to them in some writings, even if they are not too clear. The contemporary historian Johannes of Winterthur records that the Schwyz contingent at the battle of Morgarten wore foot spikes. Subsequently it was said that the historian was merely referring to heavily nailed footwear. But probably the record is concerned with those irons with four spikes which, bound to the middle of the foot, were being used at a later date by foresters and woodcutters, and which are the real "ancestors" of the crampons of more recent date.

High passes with their glaciers, such as the Col d'Hérens (3462 metres) and the Col Collon (3117 metres) were regularly used and complete herds of cattle driven over them. Perhaps there was some connection with the fact that the men of the middle ages, and most of all the mountain dwellers, were far closer to death than the educated people of our own times; there was, furthermore, the chance of commercial gain. In Les Haudères there is a field which is still called "Marché des Langobards" (Langobards' Market) where the Lombardy traders bought up the black Ehring cattle for slaughter and drove them away over the passes. In 1364 the community of St Martin in the Val d'Hérens asked the Bishop of Sion to send a German-speaking priest so that he could hear confession from the people of Zermatt who were on a pilgrimage to Valeria in Sion. From this it is clear that the inhabitants of Zermatt regularly crossed the Col d'Hérens as pilgrims in order to continue via Bricola and on through the Val d'Hérens to Sion. On three occasions, in 1517, 1525 and 1529, the provincial council of Valais ordered the muletrack over the Col Collon to be destroyed as the defence of too many alpine passes was a strain on their resources during the wars which were then raging.

The mountaineer and historian Heinrich Dübi, for many years editor of the Swiss Alpine Club's Yearbook, has relegated to the world of legend the tradition that the glacier passes between the Bernese Oberland and the Valais, among them the Wetter-lücke, were in regular use. Today we must still reserve final judgement on these traditional accounts, since we now know of such movement over the passes from a number of recorded episodes. Certainly, far too little is known about the very considerable changes in the extent of the glaciers which have played an important part in making them negotiable or not. Some passes must have been more readily usable when the glacier had retreated some distance along the lateral moraines, others when the glacier was at its maximum and the fissures in the rock were filled, presenting a surface more or less free of cracks.

The period in which mountaineering first appears in Swiss literature can be fixed as after 1500. This was the period of change in the history of the West known as the "Renaissance" or the "Age of Humanism". If "Renaissance" is more concerned with art and political systems, then "Humanism" describes the change in man's outlook. Previously he had regarded the world as the expression of a divine will to create and its phenomena were explained by religious and secular stories handed down from one generation to another. Recognition and comprehension of what happened in the world and in nature were sought in the Holy Scriptures and from the few books which had survived from antiquity, principally those of Aristotle, but not from nature itself.

Now, however, the age of experiment was beginning. Experiment meant "trying out". Mankind sought to build up a new conception of the world based on observation and experience. Where man had previously *believed*, now he wanted *proof*. He no longer wished to be a creature of fate, to some extent a piece of flotsam washed this way and that along the stream of world events. He began to determine his own bearings, he desired to have control of his own destiny, he started to act.

It was not altogether a matter of chance that this period saw the first literary descriptions of mountain climbing in the Swiss Alps. The first one was by the humanist and later burgomaster and reformer of St Gallen, Joachim Watt, known by his humanist name of Vadianus, who in 1518 climbed the Pilatus (2120 metres). The motive was typical of the age: Vadian wanted to obtain proof to destroy the superstition that the ghost of Pontius Pilate lay in the lake of Mount Pilatus. Among the company which ascended the mountain with him, it can scarcely be doubted that some were motivated by that primitive, not wholly explicable desire of the human being to climb mountains purely for the pleasure of doing so and to aspire to reach the point where one can go no further. The first ascent of Pilatus was followed in 1536 by the first ascent of the Stockhorn by a jovial company of learned men revelling in the spirit of the ancients, drawn from the Reformed theologians of Berne under the leadership of the local guide Peter Kunz, who had been a priest in Erlenbach and Zweisimmen between 1517 and 1535. The most learned of the company was Rhellicanus, otherwise Johannes Müller from Rellikon (Zürich), who was Professor of Greek and Theology in Berne and who left a long report on the expedition written in Latin hexameter *De Stockhornias*—composed as a humorous account parodied from ancient writings. When resting at the Hinterstockensee, the country is pictured as being peopled by nymphs.

But modern science breaks in; now one speaks of the stars, the animals and hunting; for the first time, alpine flowers are described, milk and cheese are praised and enjoyed with venison and wine. We also learn that men from Erlenbach, acquainted with the mountains, hunted mountain deer in this region—apparently expeditions to these exalted regions were a regular thing for these people. Inspired by the Bernese theologians, the Zürich naturalist, Konrad Gessner, made the second ascent of Pilatus in 1555, followed in 1557 by the Bernese priest Benedict Marti, known as Aretius, who climbed the Stockhorn and the Niesen in the same year and also left behind a record of his observations which even now strike a modern note. Finally, in 1574 the Zürich humanist Josias Simler, a learned man of many parts, gathered all the accounts of the Alps recorded up till then into a single Latin publication *De Alpibus commentarius.*

The seventeenth century was not notable for any exploration of the Alps. After its early awakening, the humanist spirit had again petered out. Instead of the fresh approach to world events which had been unleashed by the pure faith in God of reformers such as Vadian and Zwingli, a rigid dogmatism and dark superstition had set in which found its expression in witch hunts. Nevertheless, some paintings appear to testify—certainly from a distance—to a completely new impression of the Alps which was closer to nature. The magnificent painting of the Grindelwald glacier by Joseph Plepp (1595–1642) in Matthew Merian's *Topographie,* some of the vignettes of Albrecht Kauw of Berne (died 1681 or 1682), Johannes Dünz (1645–1736) and of Felix Meyer of Zürich (1653–1713) throw some light on the Swiss Alps from the brilliance of seventeenth-century landscape painting.

With the dawn of the eighteenth century, the urge towards natural research arose for the second time, leading into the Age of Enlightenment which brought to the Swiss Alps the eminent trio Johann Jacob Scheuchzer of Zürich (1672–1733), Albrecht von Haller of Berne (1708–1777) and Horace Bénédict de Saussure of Geneva (1740 to 1799). Scheuchzer, a doctor and widely experienced naturalist, stands right at the threshold of the new enlightened age. In the copperplate etchings of his countless works we meet dragons and all kinds of monsters side by side with modern observed fossils and one of the first records of the strata on Lake Uri. In the *Physica Sacra,* an enormous edition of the Bible with etchings of scientific phenomena, an attempt is made to reconcile the emerging natural sciences with the beliefs of Biblical revelation. Scheuchzer was not a real alpinist. On the many alpine excursions which he made with his students between 1702 and 1711, he kept to the well-trodden paths.

Albrecht von Haller also did not climb to the upper regions of rock and ice. It was his botanical interest which took him into the mountains, and here the poet was awakened in him when as a young man in 1729 his poem *Die Alpen* met with such enthusiastic response throughout the world. Formerly regarded as a source of terror, the Alps were now being described as a region of sublimation. The ancient longing of mankind for a paradise where the pure man could live in harmony with nature was projected into the description of the Alps and reflected back into the world right up to our own day. From there it was only a short step to J. J. Rousseau's return to Nature and it was the powerful genius of Haller, who as poet, doctor, physiologist and botanist, inspired Goethe also to visit the Alps.

Horace Bénédict de Saussure was the first man to penetrate into the really high regions of ice, including an ascent in 1787 of the highest mountain of the whole alpine range, Mont Blanc (4807 metres). At de Saussure's suggestion, two men from Chamonix, the doctor Michel Gabriel Paccard and the crystallographer Jacques Balmat, had reached the top for the first time the year before and had made a reconnaissance for de Saussure's grand expedition. As geologist and physicist, de Saussure was more specialised than Scheuchzer and Haller and did not have the same universality—an indication of the way modern science was to develop from that period onwards. The results of de Saussure's abundant research activities were for the most part recorded in the four volumes *Voyages dans les Alpes* (Neuchâtel 1779–1796), which came after the much admired publication in 1760 of *Die Eisgebirge des Schweizerlandes* by Gottlieb Sigmund Gruner of Berne. It was during the earlier years of the period that the famous lifework appeared of a Benedictine priest from Disentis, Placidus à Spescha (1752 to 1833), who was an indefatigable explorer of the Alps of the Grisons and Central Switzerland, collecting an abundant harvest of observations and specimens. The list of high peaks of which à Spescha made the first ascent is an imposing one, including

View of the ice mountains and glaciers in the Grindelwald
Drawing by F. Meyer.
Engraving by A. Zingg.
Reproduced from *Die Eisgebirge des Schweizerlandes* by Gottlieb Sigmund Gruner.
Vol. I, pp. 76/77. Berne 1760.
(Swiss Alpine Museum, Berne.)

Rheinwaldhorn, Piz Aul, Piz Terri, Piz Scharboden, the Güferhorn, Piz Giuf, Oberalpstock, Badus, Piz Urlaun and others. But his supreme ambition to climb the Tödi remained unfulfilled.

At that time, alpine surveying received its first major impetus. At first Swiss cartographers, relief model builders and surveyors were not only concerned to produce workable aids for finding a route through the maze of valleys, peaks, ridges and glaciers, but also to depict the whole majesty and overwhelming beauty of the alpine regions. Thus the art of making relief maps was born and later on, with the advance in printing methods, it was possible to reproduce a map in various colours to reflect the contours. After some twenty years' work, Franz Ludwig Pfyffer of Lucerne completed in the year 1775 the first large-scale relief map of Central Switzerland, which is now the main feature of the collection in the Lucerne Glacier Garden. He was followed by the Aarau manufacturer Johann Rudolf Meyer (1739–1813), who produced at his own expense and shortly before the eclipse of the old Confederation a relief model, very accurate for the time, of the whole of Switzerland on the scale 1:60000. The somewhat superficial but rapid survey sufficient for the requirements was carried out by the Strasbourg engineer-surveyor Johann Heinrich Weiss, but the construction of the model was the work of Joachim Eugen Müller, a gifted workman of humble origins from Engelberg. Napoleon I recognised the strategic value of this relief model at once and bought it, so that this superb product of Swiss alpine surveying can only be seen in the Invalides museum in Paris. Following these relief models, the first combined atlas of Switzerland was completed between the years 1796 and 1802, published in sixteen sheets (scale 1:120000) together with an overall map and etched in copperplate. Here for the first time the whole of the Alps is shown in free hatching from a vertical perspective, whereas previously the mountains had always been represented by an angled view.

Weiss and Müller had made a number of ascents to some of the more accessible heights in order to produce their relief maps, taking surveys and measurements as they went, recording their triangulations, and making plaster models. The very high and extensive ranges of the eternal snows of the Bernese and Valais Alps were therefore beyond their reach. This was the immediate reason for making the next major stage in the history of Swiss mountaineering, the first ascent of the Jungfrau (4158 metres) on August 3, 1811, by the sons of Johann Rudolf Meyer, Johann Rudolf Jr and Hieronymus Meyer. In an effort to improve on the maps published by their father, they carried out during the years 1811 and 1812 extensive expeditions into the high Alps between Lötschenlücke and Grimsel. There is a story that the Finsteraarhorn (4273 metres) was reached in 1812 by the Meyer brothers' three guides, but there have been good grounds for this being subsequently discounted. This ascent was first achieved by two guides of the glacier explorer and geologist from Solothurn, Franz Joseph Hugi, who undertook some adventurous expeditions in the area of the Rottal up the Jungfrau and the Finsteraarhorn. While Hugi had to remain below because of an injury to his foot, his guides, Jakob Leuthold and Johann Währen, reached the highest point on August 19, 1828.

In the first decades of the nineteenth century, the idyllic approach to the Alps heralded by Haller, Rousseau and Goethe, led to another surge of enthusiasm for them. The actual members of this movement were principally the Swiss miniature school, so called because their landscape views were almost invariably in the form of small paintings. These miniature painters sometimes worked in oils, but more often in soft water colours, and most of all developed the reproduction of their works in copper engravings or etchings, in outline first of all and then coloured individually by hand. This burst of activity was opened up in the eighteenth century by Johann Ludwig Aberli (1723–1786), a native of Winterthur who worked in Berne, followed by Caspar Wolf (1735–1798), P. Birmann (1758–1844), Franz Niklaus König (1765 to 1831) and the two Lorys, the father Gabriel Ludwig (1763–1840) and his son Mathias Gabriel (1784–1846) to mention only the most prominent. Franz Niklaus König, who lived for a time in Unterseen, together with Niklaus Friedrich von Mülinen, the chief magistrate of Berne, was the main initiator of the impressive Feast of the Alpine Shepherds of Unspunnen, which was staged in 1805 and 1808 before a large audience of visitors from inside and outside Switzerland. After all the years of humiliation which followed the downfall of the old Confederation and the years of occupation by foreign armies, Switzerland turned to its Alps for inspiration to gather new strength and confidence. The achievements of the period in the Alps, such as the ascent of the Jungfrau by the Meyer brothers, must be seen in the light of this awakened national consciousness.

The feeling for nature grew among the romantics. The composer Felix Mendelssohn and the poet Lord Byron stayed in and around Interlaken and on the Wengernalp, finding new inspiration there. The painters followed. The exquisite but timid style of the miniature art school had to give way to something bolder. Gloomy narrow defiles, high walls of rock partially hidden by clouds, summits shimmering down from the distant blue skies, windswept pines and landscapes breathing a spirit of melancholy against the setting sun were the expression of a new relationship to the mountains by impetuous men wholly absorbed in their dedicated task. Maximilian de Meuron (1785–1868) could still produce his high mountain landscapes on a comparatively small canvas; Alexandre Calame (1810–1864) came wholly under the intoxicating influence of the high mountains which inspired his immense canvasses that were typical of the age.

Against this imaginative background, the great age of mountaineering was dawning. One impulse came from science, especially geology, glacier research and botany. Another came from a romantic feeling for nature, the urge of man to search out the unknown, to reach towards the light and up to the heights. The peculiar aspects of

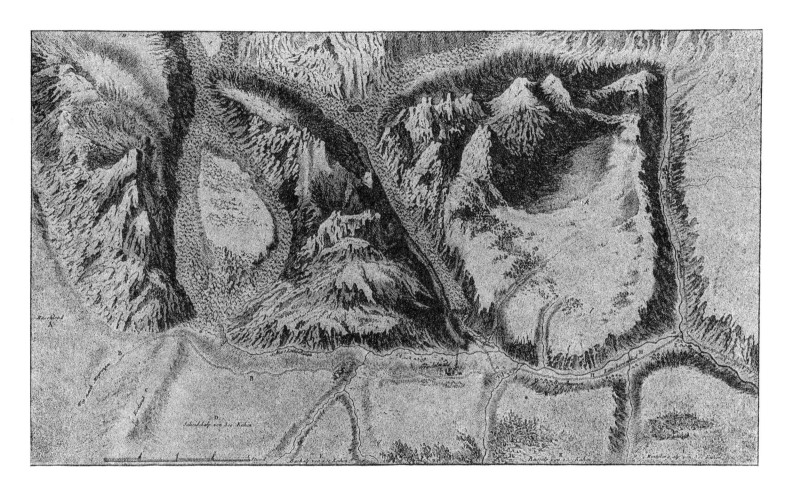

Plan of the ice valleys and glaciers in the Grindelwald
Drawing by A. Herbord.
Engraving by A. Zingg.
Reproduced from *Die Eisgebirge des Schweizerlandes* by Gottlieb Sigmund Gruner.
Vol. I, pp. 90/91. Berne 1760.
(Swiss Alpine Museum, Berne.)

the human spirit were brought into the open. Every species of animal has his native ground, his habitat, in which he moves around, driven solely by the biological necessity to keep alive, and within this habitat the creature is content. Man is otherwise. In his inmost soul he carried a picture of a country where there is no suffering, no illness, no hunger, no hatred and no death. With ceaseless longing, man composes his imaginary picture and projects it into an earthly landscape. To the ancient Greeks it was the hills of Arcady; for the people of the nineteenth century it was the world of the high Alps, the goal of an unsatisfied longing, the symbol of eternity.

But there was still some feeling of guilt when faced with the irrational features of mountain climbing. Every expedition into the mountains had to be justified by a rationale, a scientific objective. Just what it was that sparked off this urge can be gathered from a letter of the zoologist and geologist, Ludwig Rütimeyer (1825–1895), who wrote from Palermo: "I would gladly give the whole of Italy for just one ramble through forest and meadow, over rocks and stones, on our hills of the Emmental or on the rugged ridges of the Oberland."

Thus, in the course of their vigorous activities, Swiss men of science acquired a feeling

15

of awe for the works of nature. Probably the most impressive was Oswald Heer (1809–1883), who made another attempt to bring the factual basis of natural science into harmony with belief in divine revelation. For his address on the occasion of the centenary celebrations of the Institute of Natural Research in Zürich in 1847, he chose as his theme "Concerning the Harmony of Creation". Soon the main centre of attention was the circle of scientists from Neuchâtel gathered round Louis Agassiz (1807–1873) and Edward Desor (1811–1882) who, in the years between 1840 and 1845, made systematic studies of the glaciers, using a permanent headquarters under a crag of the medial moraine of the Unteraar Glacier which was dubbed "Hôtel Neuchâtelois". Their prodigious findings were recorded in impressive pages full of statistics. In the course of their work, several more summits were climbed for the first time, such as the Gross-Lauteraarhorn and the Rosenhorn in 1842 and 1844 by Desor, and the Hasle-Jungfrau in the Wetterhorn group by Agassiz in 1845. Agassiz, a natural scientist in many fields, later on devoted his attention to other branches, making a name for himself principally by his monumental work on the fishes of Switzerland, and passing his later years in the United States as a geologist.

The foremost alpine geologists of the pioneer period were the Zürich professor Arnold Escher von der Linth (1807–1872), son of the Hans Conrad Escher who became famous for his canalisation of the Linth, the Berne professor Bernhard Studer (1794–1887), Gottlieb Ludwig Theobald (1810–1869) who worked at the Cantonal School in Chur, Karl Ludwig Rütimeyer (1825–1895), a native of Emmental who worked in Basle, achieving world fame as a zoologist, and Edmund von Fellenberg (1838–1902), the mining engineer and private tutor from Berne, the outstanding man of daring and audacity among the Swiss of the "supreme age". The St Gallen merchant Friedrich von Tschudi (1820–1886) became famous as a research worker into the animal life of the Alps, and the Basle lawyer Hermann Christ (1833–1933) was, after Albrecht von Haller, the most important botanist and plant ecologist of the Swiss Alps. The most impressive literary record to be published during the century of scientific exploration of the Alps is to be found in Oswald Heer's magnificent work *Die Urwelt der Schweiz* (The Origins of Switzerland) published in 1865. Beautifully written, yet simple enough for anyone to understand, it gives a comprehensive portrayal of the original geology and plant ecology in the distant past of Switzerland in general and of the alpine regions in particular.

Mapmaking of the alpine regions was also on an impressive scale; this was the period in which the Dufour map appeared, the most famous of all maps of Switzerland. The most energetic alpinist among the cartographers during the Dufour period was Johann Wilhelm Fortunat Coaz (1822–1918) from the Grisons, who rose to become chief forest inspector, first for the Grisons and finally for the whole Confederation. In the course of his map-making surveys he made a large number of first ascents, such as the Hoch-Ducan and the Flüela Weisshorn in 1845, the west peak of Piz Kesch in

Following double page
The sun rises behind the
Rotwand. The sky is aflame
over the black outline of the
Vorarlberg peaks. The
fascinated mountaineer watches
the oldest spectacle in the
world, which he has eagerly
looked forward to seeing after a
cold night in his tent.

1846, Piz Quadervals in 1848, Piz Corvatsch, Piz Tschierva and the highest peak of the Grisons, Piz Bernina (4049 metres), in 1850. Later Coaz made a name for himself with a series of publications describing the forest features of the Alps and plantations as avalanche barriers.

Besides the topographers and scientists there was a third group who at that time were called *montanists*, tireless and often adventurous travellers through the Alps. Though not trained or active as scientists, the reports they made of their travels contributed much towards alpine topography and provided the names of many of the more remote peaks and passes by their wanderings through the Alps, often surprising in their extent and frequency. Among them were Melchior Ulrich from Zürich (1802 to 1893), Gottlieb Studer from Berne (1804–1890) and Johann Jakob Weilenmann from St Gallen (1819–1896); also, Ivan von Tschudi, brother of Friedrich, from St Gallen (1816–1887) and Albert Hoffmann-Burckhardt from Basle (1826–1896). Like Oswald Heer, Melchior Ulrich was originally a theologian; Weilenmann, Tschudi and Hoffmann-Burckhardt were prosperous merchants, who were able to devote all their enthusiasm to the Alps, Weilenmann being also a bold, tough and individualistic climber. For really high ascents he engaged mountain guides. The most extraordinary character was Gottlieb Studer, a cousin of Bernhard Studer, notary by profession, later Federal Governor for the Berne district. As a legacy of his mountain expeditions, which took him all over the Swiss Alps and many other areas as far as Norway, he left nearly 2000 drawings and panoramas, among them some 700 panorama sheets, in aquatint or fine water-colour, many of them several feet long, which he sketched in an incredibly short time on the spot, applying the finishing touches later.

In the mid-1850s the British joined in these activities. With the exception of the Irishman Professor John Tyndall (1820–1893) who made scientific investigations into glacier behaviour between 1860 and 1865, 1887 and 1889 in the Zermatt, Aletsch Glacier and Pontresina areas, English, Scots and Irish were predominantly attracted to mountaineering as a sport. First ascents were the principal factors in assessing results. In 1857 the Alpine Club was founded mostly from the upper and intellectual classes of Victorian England, which required from its members not only an acceptable social status but also some alpine achievement every year. Among the members we find principally lawyers, Anglican clergymen, senior army and naval officers, headmasters and teachers from public schools, bankers and merchants, landowners, a few medical men, scientists and engineers. Many members were not active in any profession. For the members, many of whom were well-to-do, the thirst for adventure came as a reaction to the transformation of labour and working by technical developments which were then in full swing in England. The outstanding personalities among the British who were active in the Alps during that period were John Ball (1818–1889), the founder of the Alpine Club and author of a guide to the western Alps; the Rev. Charles Hudson (1828–1865) who was killed after the first ascent of the Matterhorn, but was regarded as the safest mountain climber and the leading authority in the Alpine Club and described by Charles Kingsley as "a Christian athlete who feared God and who could cover a hundred miles in a hundred hours"; John Tyndall, mentioned previously, one of the leading glacier explorers; Sir Leslie Stephen (1832–1904), at one time in holy orders, who wrote a pamphlet in defence of atheism, "making long walks instead of long prayers" according to R. Mortimer, and spent most of his time describing the irrational aspects of mountaineering, eulogising them to the point of creating an alpine mystique; A. W. Moore (1811–1887), who is also numbered among the pioneer climbers of the highest peaks in the Caucasus; Thomas Stuart Kennedy (1841–1894) who grew up in Feldkirch, owned extensive property in Scotland, a man aesthetic rather than reserved by nature, who was the first to conceive the feasibility of climbing the Matterhorn from Zermatt; and, not perhaps quite so deserving of the fame he achieved in making the first ascent of the Matterhorn, Edward Whymper (1840–1911), who as book illustration engraver did not quite fit into the illustrious circle and perhaps for that reason was spurred on to undertake exceptional feats.

At the same time as the British appeared on the scene, the supreme age of the Swiss mountain guides opened up. Among them may be mentioned Christian Almer (1826 to 1897), the quiet, flaxen-haired mountain peasant from Grindelwald with his firm step and sure grip, and Melchior Anderegg (1827–1914), the imperturbable, quiet-spoken mountain farmer, woodcarver and hunter from Zaun, near Meiringen, with the strength of a bear but at the same time a highly gifted artist. These two can be regarded as the most outstanding, acquiring in later years a legendary status. Scarcely less famous are Ulrich Lauener (1821–1900) and his brother Christian (1826–1891) from Lauterbrunnen, Johann Baumann (1830–1899) and Peter Baumann (1833 to 1921), Peter Bohren (1822–1882) and Ulrich Kaufmann (1840–1917) from Grindelwald, Johann Joseph Bennen (1824–1864) from Lax in Goms, Peter Knubel (1833 to 1919) from St Niklaus in Valais, Hans Grass (1828–1902) from Pontresina and many other names which contributed to the glory of the "supreme age". To a younger generation belong Alexander Burgener (1846–1910) from Eisten in Valais and Christian Klucker (1853–1928) from Fex.

The British use the term the "golden age of mountaineering" to describe the period starting with the first attempts at climbing the Alps in 1854 and reaching its zenith with the first ascent of the Matterhorn in 1865. In this single decade the British and their Swiss guides accomplished more than sixty first ascents in the Swiss Alps. Among them were in 1854 the Wetterhorn, starting from Grindelwald, by Alfred Wills, together with Ulrich Lauener, Peter Bohren and other guides, joined by Christian Almer and Ulrich Kaufmann, who had made an independent start; in 1855, the Monte Rosa (western summit) by G. and S. Smith with Ulrich Lauener; in 1857, the

Mönch by S. Porges with Christian Almer, Ulrich and Ch. Kaufmann; the Kleine Schreckhorn by E. Anderson with Christian Almer and Peter Bohren; in 1858, the Eiger by Ch. Barrington with Christian Almer and Peter Bohren; the Dom by J. L. Davies with J. zum Taugwald; in 1859, the Aletschhorn by F. F. Tuckett with J. J. Bennen and P. Bohren, the Bietschhorn by Leslie Stephen with two guides, and the Rimpfischhorn by Leslie Stephen with two guides; in 1860, the Blümlisalphorn by Leslie Stephen with Melchior Anderegg and P. Simond, the Grand Combin by Delville with E. and G. Bailley, the Alphubel by Leslie Stephen with Melchior Anderegg; in 1861, the Gross Schreckhorn by Leslie Stephen with Christian and Peter Michel and Ulrich Kaufmann, the Monte Rosa (north end) by T. F. and E. N. Buxton with M. Payot, the Lyskamm by J. F. Hardy with eight other British and eight guides, the Weisshorn by John Tyndall with J. J. Bennen; in 1862, the Gross Fiescherhorn by A. W. Moore and H. B. George with Christian Almer and Ulrich Kaufmann, the Täschhorn by J. L. Davies with J. and St. Taugwalder and J. Summermatter, the Dent Blanche by T. S. Kennedy with J. B. Croz and J. Kronig, and the Disgrazia by Leslie Stephen and T. S. Kennedy with Melchior Anderegg; in 1863, the Dent d'Hérens and Monte Rosa (Parrotspitze) by R. S. Macdonald and F. C. Grove with Melchior Anderegg and P. Perren, Piz Palü by E. N. Buxton with four companions and three guides, Piz Roseg (north summit) by E. S. Bircham with A. Flury and F. Jenny; in 1864, the Balmhorn by F. and H. Walker with M. and J. Anderegg, the Jungfrau from Rottal by Leslie Stephen, R. S. Macdonald and F. C. Grove with M. and J. Anderegg and J. Bischoff, the Zinal-Rothorn by Leslie Stephen and F. C. Grove with M. and J. Anderegg; in 1865, the Jungfrau from the Wengernalp by H. B. George and G. Young with Chr. Almer and J. Baumann, the Obergabelhorn by A. W. Moore and H. Walker with J. Anderegg, the Grand Cornier by Edward Whymper with Christian Almer and F. Biener, Piz Roseg (main peak) by A. W. Moore and H. Walker with J. Anderegg, and—as the most sensational achievement—the Matterhorn by the Rev. Charles Hudson, Edward Whymper, Lord Francis Douglas and Robert Douglas Hadow with the guides Michel Croz from Chamonix and Peter Taugwalder (father and son) from Zermatt. The chief contributors to this achievement were the experienced Hudson and the elder Taugwalder, who recognised clearly the possibility of following the Hörnli ridge. Whymper, who had obstinately been pursuing for many years the first ascent from Breuil and for that reason had fallen out with the local pioneers Jean Antoine Carrel, César Carrel, Abbé Amé Gorret, Jean Baptiste Bich and others, joined Hudson at the last minute. He became the only survivor of the party to achieve fame; Hudson, Douglas, Hadow and Michel Groz were the victims of a dreadful disaster, while the reputation of Peter Taugwalder was destroyed by all sorts of suspicions.

Compared with these, the achievements of the Swiss "gentry" in making spectacular first ascents were few, since the Swiss were motivated principally by scientific inves-

Franz Joseph Hugi and his companions in the Rottal on the Jungfrau, 1828
Artist unknown. From *Naturhistorische Alpenreise* by Franz Joseph Hugi, Solothurn, 1830. (Swiss Alpine Museum, Berne.)

tigations, and not first ascents as ends in themselves. Nevertheless, the enterprising and active contestant Edmund von Fellenberg threw a deliberate though quite friendly challenge to the British and on his own account ascended in 1856 the Wildstrubel, in 1862 the Klein and Gross Doldenhorn and the Weisse Frau, in 1863 the Silberhorn, in 1864 the Klein Fiescherhorn, in 1865 the Lauterbrunner Breithorn and the Gross Grünhorn from the south-west, in 1866 the Mönch by the north-west, in 1867 the Bietschhorn by the western ridge and other notable achievements. On the Lauterbrunner Breithorn an actual contest in walking and climbing took place on July 31, 1865 between Edmund von Fellenberg, who had started at six o'clock from the Trachsellauenen inn with the guides Peter Michel, Peter Inäbit and Peter Egger of Grindelwald and Johann Bischoff of Lauterbrunnen, and the Englishmen Philpott and Hornby, who had left the Steinbergalp at two o'clock with Christian Almer and Christian Lauener in order to reach the Breithorn by the Petersgrat. Fellenberg was victorious and at 10.40 planted the Swiss flag on the summit. Fifteen minutes later Christian Almer erected in the snow beside it the "Tanngrotzli" which he had brought with him.

Outstanding personalities among the other Swiss were J. J. Weilenmann, who climbed 350 peaks in twenty years, of which the most important were a solo expedition to Monte Leone in 1859, the Fluchthorn with F. Pöll in 1861, the Mont Blanc de Cheilon in 1865 with J. Felley, and the Piz Buin with J. A. Specht and two guides. Melchior Ulrich was the first to reach the summit of the peak subsequently named after him, the Ulrichhorn, in the Mischabel group in 1848, the west peak of Monte Leone and the summit of the Diablerets in 1850; and with Gottlieb Studer on the Glarner Tödi in 1853. The list of Gottlieb Studer's first ascents includes twenty-two names, although Studer was not really a climber of the high Alps. Among Studer's first ascents were the Sustenhorn in 1841, the Wildhorn in 1843, the Gross Wannehorn and the Studerhorn in 1864 (both with Rudolf Lindt), as well as the Ofenhorn, the Gross Rindhorn and the Basodino. In Central Switzerland, the Düssistock and Vorab were first climbed in 1842 by Arnold Escher and the Gross Windgälle in 1848 by George Hoffmann. The Titlis had already been climbed in 1744 by the monks of the Engelberg monastery, and in 1787 by J. R. Meyer and J. E. Müller.

It was at that time that the Swiss mountaineers came together in the Swiss Alpine Club for the purpose of organising themselves better to participate in rivalry with the British in exploring and conducting their research in the Swiss Alps. During the afternoon of July 30, 1861 this objective was defined by the Berne geologist and chemist Dr Rudolf Theodor Simler (1833–1873) in a speech on the summit of the Piz Rusein in the Tödi region and immediately acted upon. On April 19, 1863 the inaugural meeting was held in the Station restaurant at Olten and on September 5, 1863, the first constitution was agreed. The young club, to which all the leading Swiss mountaineers of that period belonged, aimed primarily at the scientific exploration of the

Alps, publication of reports and opening up the Alps to travellers by the provision of simple overnight accommodation. In the year of its inauguration, there were eight sections with 257 members; a hundred years later, in 1963, there were 92 sections with 44,649 members. In the year of inauguration the first primitive club hut was erected on the Tödi; in 1913 there were 75 and in 1963 they had increased to 148, including eight huts of the independent Academic Alpine Club.

The Matterhorn disaster of 1865 interrupted to some extent the enthusiasm of the British but did not stultify it. The prodigious number of summits climbed became less. First ascents became less frequent and covered only the less well-known peaks or routes of exceptional difficulty. Already the British were transferring their main activity to other areas, mainly in the Dauphiné, but soon afterwards also to the Caucasus, the Himalayas and the Andes. But even so, the seventies brought a revival which the British call the "silver age of mountaineering". It lasted until 1882 when the first ascent was made of the Aiguille du Géant in the Mont Blanc region by the Sella brothers from Biella in Italy and by W. Graham with Jean-Joseph Maquignaz from Breuil as guide. The outstanding event of this silver age occurred under the leadership of the Englishman A. F. Mummery (born 1856) who disappeared on the Nanga Parbat in the Himalayas on or after 1895. He did much to develop the technique of rock-climbing, introducing a new style of mountaineering which naturally was now being developed for the most part outside Switzerland, in the pinnacles of the Mont Blanc region and in the Eastern Alps. Mummery, a capricious, enterprising and daring enthusiast, made many of his expeditions and ascents without any guides, sometimes even without companions, and thus pioneered the fashion of guideless climbing, the principal innovators from outside Switzerland being the Austrian Count Emil Zsigmondy (1861–1885) and Ludwig Purtscheller (1849–1900), the Englishman Charles Pilkington (1850–1919) and the Frenchmen Victor and Pierre Puiseux (1820–1883 and 1855–1928) who occasionally came to Switzerland. Purtscheller was the first to cross the Monte Rosa from Macugnaga to Zermatt and the Bietschhorn from the south, Pilkington making the first guideless ascent of the Finsteraarhorn in 1881.

It was during this period that there appeared the American William Augustus Brevoort Coolidge (1850–1926), who came to England at the age of fourteen, became an Anglican clergyman, but soon abandoned orders, and from 1896 made his home in Grindelwald in order to devote himself entirely to the Alps. He followed the traditional methods, made his expeditions principally in the regions of snow and ice, accompanied only by guides from the locality, of whom Christian Almer from 1868 onwards was his trusted companion for seventeen years. Accompanied on most of them also by this enterprising aunt, Miss Meta Brevoort, whose name looms large in the history of female alpinism, and the sheepdog Tschingel from the Lötschental, he built up an astonishing record of alpine climbing. At the end he could look back on the ascent of some 1700 peaks and passes, of which 74 were first ascents and first explorations, the majority of them in the Dauphiné, where Coolidge was the first human being to penetrate into some of the regions. Tschingel achieved the record of alpine expeditions by a dog, including 30 peaks and 36 passes beginning with the Blümlisalp and crowned by Mont Blanc. Coolidge was very active as a writer, principally of articles for encyclopaedias and magazines, guidebooks to the Alps and some major works on alpine history—all of them written in a cold, prosaic style bereft of any excursions into literary enthusiasm, but factually most valuable. By making winter ascents of the Wetterhorn, the Jungfrau and the Schreckhorn, Coolidge must also be regarded as a pioneer of winter alpine exploration.

It was about this time that a school of thought was developing among the Swiss which found its expression in the words of Carl Egger "the spiritualisation of mountaineering". Besides the natural scientists headed at the time by the geologist Albert Heim (1849–1937) and the botanist Carl Schröter (1855–1939), both of them professors at the Federal Technical High School in Zürich, and who led the field in alpine exploration, there were also theologians, historians, authors and philosophers who came under the spell of the Alps—and finally, those who came to the high mountains simply for the experience. This movement began with Eugène Rambert (1830–1886), Professor of French literature at Lausanne University and at the Federal Technical High School, an enthusiastic mountaineer and the moving spirit of the Swiss Alpine Club. Discussions arose as to the deeper meaning of mountaineering, and Eugène Rambert gave the answer: "The mountaineer is basically a man who loves adventure and for whom modern society and its way of life are nothing but a prison."

These words could be just as true today and for this reason a mountaineer will struggle hard to ensure that this prison life and all the feverish restlessness of the technological world will be kept away from his alpine retreats.

In the footsteps of Eugène Rambert, to this cult of alpinism came other leading lights, represented by Emile Javelle (1847–1883), the enthusiastic head of a boys' school in Vevey, who crossed Mont Blanc with his fifteen-year old pupils from Courmayeur to Chamonix, followed by the Berne High School teacher and historian Heinrich Dübi (1848–1942), for many years editor of the Swiss Alpine Club Yearbook and, after Coolidge, the leading historian of Swiss mountaineering, whose most famous achievements were the first crossing of the Jungfrau from Rottal to the Wengernalp (1873) and the first ascent of the Gross Fiescherhorn over the north-west ridge. Further, Andreas Fischer (1865–1912), a guide from a family of mountain guides from Zaun near Meiringen, primary school teacher in Thun, secondary school teacher in Grindelwald, doctor in German literature, high-school teacher in Berne and later in Basle, with an iron constitution, his enthusiasm wholly dedicated to the mountains and yet a model of caution throughout his life of travel and prodigious achievement in the Alps of Dauphiné, the Dolomites and the Caucasus, until his death during a

Gottlieb Studer and his companions negotiating the wide crevasses on the Jungfrau by means of a ladder on August 14, 1842
Artist not mentioned, probably drawn by Studer himself. Title page for the first volume of *Topographische Mitteilungen aus dem Alpengebirge*, edited by Gottlieb Studer, Berne and St Gallen, 1843. (Swiss Alpine Museum, Berne.)

night of dreadful storm on the Aletschhorn. His work *Travels Through the High Mountain Regions in the Alps and the Caucasus* published posthumously, is his great contribution to alpine literature.

It was in this period, too, that there arose another group of individual mountaineers on Swiss territory, independent of Pilkington, Gardiner, Zsigmondy, Purtscheller and Puiseux, who travelled without guides but whose object was not scientific exploration or to achieve any special records, but to seek self-purification and inner contemplation and who therefore wished to travel alone or in the company of only a few trusted friends. Of this group, the main protagonists were the brothers Paul and Charles Montandon (1858–1948 and 1862–1923). Of the two, Paul, by his high ethics, his combination of boldness and caution, and not least by his minutely recorded experiences in more than a hundred articles and publications, truly became the instructor of a whole generation of Swiss mountaineers. Born in humble circumstances, Charles became a lawyer in Berne; Paul, through his marriage, became the owner of a tileworks in Glockental near Thun. Paul's seventeen thick volumes of itineraries comprise forty ascents of mountains over 4000 metres, over 600 lower peaks and fifty first ascents of and new routes to peaks over 3000 metres. The list, attributable to his wife, before her marriage Sarah Koenig, who was his most faithful companion on these mountain excursions, includes eighteen peaks over 4000 metres and 148 other prominent summits. Charles' list includes twenty-three first ascents and six new passes, though these do not exhaust the whole of either Paul's or Charles' achievements. From the more illuminating of Paul's descriptions, there is the first guideless ascent of the Eiger on August 18, 1878, with three companions, the oldest being twenty-three the youngest sixteen. One passage from the book of excursions can be taken to express the feelings of that generation of young mountaineers: "Up we climb, enraptured by the marvellous beauty of the night of a full moon. How our young hearts expand! Out of hearing on the other side of the valley, we can see the silver torrent of the Staubbach rushing down. In the distance is the gleam of the eternal glacier. How closely the silence of nature clings to us insignificant human beings, making us one with eternity!"

But the time was drawing near when the profound silences of nature were no longer so precious to men. In the spirit of almost naïve optimism of the tourist epoch, it was thought that as many people as possible should be given the opportunity to experience the mountains, and the first railways were built to the mountain peaks. In 1871 and 1874 the two railways up the Rigi were opened from Vitznau and Arth, followed by the railways on the Pilatus (1888), the Brienzer Rothorn and the Rochers de Naye (1892), the Gornergrat (1898), to mention only the most important, and in 1912 the railway tracks reached to the Jungfraujoch. There was talk of a cable railway for tobogganing over the Aletsch glacier and a lift up to the Matterhorn. The Swiss Alps ceased to be an area for pioneers. All the peaks had been reached and provided with names and huts; the second major cartography programme for Switzerland, the Siegfried atlas, was completed shortly after the turn of the century and showed no territory as unknown. The Swiss Alpine Club, which had agreed every year since 1863 to define a particular area for systematic research and exploration by the club, concluded this activity in 1900/1901 and no longer defined any club area. Publication of the special Club maps also declined. The first comprehensive publications on geology and botany appeared. From then on the scientists transferred their researches from the systematic to the minute, withdrawing from the field to pursue their activities in the workshop and laboratory. For the map-maker, surveys based on air photographs replaced a good part of the work on the ground.

New activities were opened up. Winter tourism started with snow-rackets and soon with skis—no longer with the same spirit of the pioneers in alpine exploration, nor in the interests of scientific research, but only for recreation and a love of sport. In 1896, the first peak of 3000 metres to be reached on skis was the Oberalpstock by Professor Wilhelm Paulke and Victor de Beauclair. Between January 18 and 23, 1897, these two, with some other German companions, travelled on skis from the Grimsel over the Oberaarjoch, Grünhornlücke, Aletsch Glacier and Belalp to Brigue. The development of mass tourism both summer and winter led in 1902 to a highly developed rescue organisation by the Swiss Alpine Club which now consists of 130 rescue stations with 1800 trained staff on hand and over 100 rescue dogs.

But even so there were some important achievements to be made. Among them must be mentioned principally the first negotiation of the north face of the Eiger on August 20, 1932, by Hans Lauper, a medical man from Berne working in Zürich, Alfred Zürcher from St Gallen and the guides Joseph Knubel and Alexander Graven. The route selected was that over the eastern part of the face, covered with a thick layer of snow, and achieved in one day without any artificial aids. The ascent through the rocky western part of the face, which was finally climbed between July 21 and 24, 1938, by Anderl Heckmair and Ludwig Voerg from Munich and Heinrich Harrer and Fritz Kasparek from Vienna in the teeth of considerable objective dangers and employing artificial aids, was already overshadowed by a strident lust for achievement on the part of a Nazi Germany and by the commercialised and sensation-hungry agencies of modern communication. Since then, the Eigernordwand has been repeatedly the object of similar unsavoury events and up to 1962 the thirty-one successful ascents had resulted in the deaths of twenty-three climbers. After the Second World War there came the second enormous upsurge of mass tourism, bringing with it a new period of funicular and cable railway building, the construction of several mountain roads and the growing popularity of air flights to the glaciers as a tourist attraction.

Most of the sensational reputation of the Alps has disappeared as a result of systematic exploration and scientific research. The modern approach to mountaineering has become that of a child which breaks a toy to see what makes it work. The child may acquire a little more knowledge, but loses another lovely toy. In the same way, we may feel some disappointment at the prospect of the alpine world stripped of its secrets now revealed in a cold scientific light, which can be reached without difficulty at any time and without any personal or prior preparation. Anyone wanting to feel for himself what the pioneer explorers of the Alps experienced, must now go to the high mountains of remote countries or search out for himself the last bit of romance and adventure on vertical walls of rock in the Alps. The tendency towards what is called advanced mountaineering is a natural and inevitable result of the complete survey of the Alps and the fact that they have been made all too accessible by road, railway or aircraft.

We shall find the correct relationship to the mountain only if we recognise that the experience of the mountains is determined not only objectively but to a considerable extent subjectively also. It comes from the meeting of man with the mountain, its intensity to a limited extent dependent upon the objective beauty of the landscape which meets the eye, but to a high degree upon the imagination of the spectator. But such preparation requires time. The sense of contented achievement which a mountain expedition gives comes from the inner excitement which stems from the anticipated view which will present itself at the summit. The longer the time spent on preparation, making plans, assembling equipment and the preliminary approach, the more the imagination is stimulated as a necessary means towards realising the supreme experience. Anyone wanting to save time on all this, who dispenses with the preliminary approach, the night in the hut or tent, but believes that this sense of achievement can be obtained by cable car or aircraft, will never realise the supreme experience of the mountains. He can perhaps take in a wonderful impression, allow the sun to do its work on his body, and then fulfil his urge for activity by racing down on his skis, which is certainly a legitimate aspiration for a person who spends most of his working day sitting or standing in one place. But this has little to do with the experience of mountaineering. The new mode of going up mountains is something quite different, not a continuation of mountaineering activity.

But there are still—and there always will be—climbers in the Alps, who see the mountains as a goal of an unfulfilled desire and therefore the symbol of eternity. It is a combination of warm friendship and love for the mountain, an attempt to penetrate to the final mystery, the satisfaction being not so much in finding the solution as in feeling that there is still something to be solved. It is one of the strangest facts of our earthly existence that in the depths of the soul the greatest pleasure and the most profound grief spring from the same source. Mountaineers who have experienced this are drawn irresistibly to the spell of the mountains often to meet the boundary which lies between life and death. The outsider, keeping strictly within all that is rational, can never understand this. He can never understand that the mountaineer is driven by motives which defy rational explanation, motives which are quite different from merely being able to say that he has stood on a summit and admired the view.

Valais, South of the Rhone

The Dents du Midi form the most westerly group of mountains in Switzerland. The Chalin hut is the starting point for the mainly difficult ascent of the St Maurice face of the Cime de l'Est. This small but extremely well-equipped hut stands on the Tête de Chalin at a height of 2590 metres. It can shelter eight climbers and belongs to the Chaussy section of the Swiss Alpine Club. The Tête de Chalin is a good observation point. The view looks down the Rhone across the Lake of Geneva and the mountains of Vaud, and up the Rhone towards the jagged horizon of the mountains of Valais, rising to more than 4000 metres.

Below: The Cime de l'Est of the Dents du Midi (3177 metres), two hours after sunset, viewed from the track leading to the Chalin hut.

The Dents du Midi with their highest peaks Haute Cime (3257 metres), Doigts (3210 metres), Dent Jaune (3186 metres), L'Eperon (3144 metres), La Cathédrale (3160 metres), La Forteresse (3164 metres) and Cime de l'Est, are a many-ridged limestone mass with gentle ascents from the west and south and some very difficult ascents, especially on the north and east sides. An ascent, outstanding in alpine performance, leads over the 700 metres high centre pillar on the St Maurice face of the Cime de l'Est. This lengthy ascent of fifth grade difficulty was first achieved on October 17, 1943, by A. Roch, P. Bonnant and R. Aubert. The view towards the range from the Lake of Geneva, with the Castle of Chillon in the foreground, is famous the world over.

Opposite page
Above: In the early morning sunrise the telelens has recorded the horizon formed by a line of well-known summits of the Valais. The Dent de Morcles (2969 metres) at the extreme right is a favourite goal for week-end climbers. On the extreme left is the southern ridge of the Grand Muveran (3051 metres), which is linked to the Dent de Morcles by a long ridge. In the centre, the Haut de Cry massif (2969 metres). In the far background, the Wildhorn (3247 metres).
Below: The jagged horizon of the Valais peaks rising more than 4000 metres against the morning sky. From left to right, the most prominent peaks are the Weisshorn, Zinalrothorn, Obergabelhorn, Dent Blanche, Matterhorn, Dent d'Hérens, Mont Blanc de Cheilon.

The famous track known as the Haute Route runs east to west along this most majestic range of peaks in the Swiss Alps, and is used by numerous skiers, especially in springtime, to cross the mountains from Saas Fee to Chamonix or vice versa.

Opposite page
Above: The Col d'Argentière (3544 metres) with the Aiguilles Rouges and (extreme left) the Mont Dolent (3820 metres). The Mont Dolent is a gracefully shaped mountain and one of the most stimulating peaks for skiers. Its summit is the point where the frontiers of Italy, France and Switzerland meet. The Col d'Argentière can be reached on skis from the Argentière hut across the Tour Noir glacier, but a descent into Valais is impossible. This wonderful ski excursion often includes the ascent of the Tour Noir (3835 metres).
Below: The route over the Col du Chardonnet and the Fenêtre de Saleina is the classic part of the Haute Route between the Argentière depression and the extensive Trient plateau. To the south the Aiguilles Dorées form the boundary of the Trient plateau, a favourite area for climbing some excellent granite. The extensive *firn* plain is a popular glacier airfield, from which the Aiguille du Tour (3540 metres) can be easily climbed. The descent to Trient involves a difference in height of 2000 metres. To the left is the Trient hut, belonging to the Diablerets section of the SAC and the Swiss Ladies' Alpine Club.

Right: The right-hand lateral moraine of the Corbassière glacier forms the upper section of the ascent to the Panossière hut on the Grand Combin. The Combin de Corbassière (3715 metres), which here rises above the Corbassière glacier, lies in front of the Grand Combin. The ascent to it is a first-class ski excursion during the spring which culminates in the majestic scenery of the ice-fall from the Grand Combin.

The Panossière hut, belonging to the Geneva section of the SAC, lies to the right edge of the Corbassière glacier at a height of 2671 metres. It is a hut in traditional style with 61 bunks and is only equipped in summer. A stay in such a hut gives a feeling of quiet satisfaction to the mountaineer, especially when not too many people are waiting for room at the cooking range. After a hard climb to the hut with a heavy pack, or returning from a strenuous excursion, or after a snowstorm or shower of rain, there is no more delightful sound than the fire crackling in the range. Here in this humble lodging the mountaineer feels protected and safe. Amid the rude elements of nature, rock, snow and ice, the hut is a life-giving oasis. All SAC huts, with the exception of some in the Ticino and Bergell, are open to any mountaineer at any time. This testifies to the commendable trust which the owners have in the fraternity of mountaineers, a trust which is seldom abused. The mountaineer enters his particulars in the hut record book when he arrives *(opposite page, top)*, does not forget to give exact details of the tour he is planning, and places the overnight charges for accommodation and fuel in the hut collection box, or pays them later by postal cheque.

Following double page
Ascent over the Corbassière glacier. To the right the Grand Combin de Valsorey (4184 metres) and the Grand Combin de Grafeneire (4314 metres), to the left the Grand Combin de Tsessette (4141 metres). The ascent by ski over the corridor (extreme right) is threatened by ice-falls for at least an hour and in the past has been the scene of a number of fatal accidents.

Opposite page
Above: Ski climbers ascending to the breakfast rendezvous on the Grand Combin, which is above the rock pillar seen to the left of the photograph.
Below: Descent from the Panossière hut to Fionnay in the Val de Bagnes, taken in the middle of May. The snow in the upper regions is hard, but lower down, towards Fionnay, it is pleasantly flaked. The early morning is often chosen for the descent, as too strong sunshine causes the snow to become slushy. In the background, the Mont Fort (3328 metres) and the Rosa Blanche (3336 metres).

This page
Above: The Vignettes hut of the Monte Rosa section of the SAC, boldly exposed on the Col des Vignettes at a height of 3157 metres, is an important stage point on the Haute Route. Over one of the finest sections of the extensive route, Zermatt can be reached in one day from here over Col de l'Evêque, Col du Mont Brûlé and Col de Valpelline.
Below: Skiers preparing for the descent from the wide cap of the Pigne d'Arolla (3796 metres) which can be comfortably reached in two hours from the Vignettes hut. In glorious weather, a stiff *bise* whips up the snow. The Matterhorn can be seen in the background.

"This must be the most magnificent obelisk of the Alps." These words were used to describe the Matterhorn by Marcel Kunz, engineer, cartographer, author of the SAC guide to the Alps of Valais and of the most knowledgeable of mountaineers. This peak, on the Swiss-Italian frontier, rises to a height of 4477 metres in majestic isolation above the end of the valley. No other Swiss mountain has so aroused the imagination of such a large section of the population for over a century. The very name Matterhorn is synonymous for all that mountains represent. From the earliest times, the inhabitants of the valley called the great mountain "z'Hora" (the peak). The first ascent was made on July 14, 1865, by the Englishmen Edward Whymper, Charles Hudson, R. D. Hadow and Francis Douglas with the guides Michel Auguste Croz and Peter Taugwalder, father and son. It was a triumph of mountaineering history clouded, however, by the tragic sequel to the expedition. During the descent, Croz, Hudson, Hadow and Douglas fell from the shoulder overlooking the north face into the depths of the Matterhorn glacier. Whymper and the two Taugwalders owed their lives to the breaking of the rope. The track followed by the first climbers led over the northeast or Hörnli ridge, which can be easily seen in the photograph. The Hörnli ridge is the longest, but at the same time the easiest of the four Matterhorn ridges. Since the Matterhorn is formed of pure rock, climbing is best carried out under good thaw conditions. On the Hörnli ridge the greatest danger arises from falls of stone loosened by parties climbing higher up. But natural falls can also occur with surprising suddenness on this steeply rising peak.

The Zmutt ridge on the Matterhorn forms one of the finest climbing routes in the Alps. The self-reliant, well-trained mountaineer will prefer it to the Hörnli ridge. The classic path runs from the Schön-bühl hut, somewhat low down (2694 metres), to the foot of the *firn* ridge *(opposite page)*.

The *firn* ridge, the only one on the Matterhorn, can also be reached from the Hörnli hut, situated 600 metres higher up. This alternative is very much exposed to rock falls. The ascent of the Zmutt ridge is a long one. Its difficulty depends largely on the snow and ice conditions on the western slope, on which the climber has to cross the Galerie Carrel in order to reach the actual ridge some distance above *(left,* showing in the background the Dent Blanche). The first ascent was made on September 3, 1879, by A.F. Mummery with Alexander Burgener, Johann Petrus and Augustin Gentinetta.

Following double page
Left: Wintry conditions on the Matterhorn. Five guides from Zermatt, led by Heinrich Taugwalder, grandson and great-grandson of the first guides to climb the mountain, Egon Petrig, Alfons Lerjen, Richard Andenmatten and Andreas Biner survey climbing conditions on the Hörnli ridge five days before the centenary celebrations (1965) of the first ascent.

Right: Crossing from the Italian summit to the Swiss summit in June, after climbing through the Zmutt ridge. Those who wish to experience the mountain in its greatest splendour will prefer to make their ascent during the early summer. The days are long and the swarms of tourists are still to come.

Grosse Windgälle

Tödi

Spitzberge

Crispalt

Pazolastock

Badus – Six Madun

Piz Medel

Gemsstock

Piz Ravetsch

Galenstock

Gross Büelenhorn

The south-east or Furggen ridge is the steepest and most difficult of the Matterhorn ridge routes. It forms the dividing line between the east and south faces of the mountain and also the frontier between Italy and Switzerland. From the Furggen shoulder (4243 metres) the summit rises perpendicularly. The Furggen ridge has a long and dramatic history of first ascents. On August 28, 1899, Guido Rey crossed the ridge during the descent. Plenty of rope and two rope ladders made it possible to descend by the vertical precipice. Twelve years later, on September 9, 1911, Marion Piacenza with Jean Joseph Carrel and Joseph Gaspard succeeded in reaching the summit. Roped together, this party avoided negotiating the vertical section on the brittle south face. It was nearly nineteen years later, on September 2, 1930, that the path followed by Piacenza was again followed by Enzo Benedetti, Luigi Carrel (Carellino) and Maurice Bich in that they crossed the minimum distance necessary to negotiate the south face. This route is now the normal route along the Furggen ridge. The direct route for making this extremely difficult ascent involves an extensive use of pitons. It was first done on September 23, 1941, by Enzo Perin and Giacomo Chiara (second guide) led by Luigi Carrel. The Furggen ridge has remained to the present day a most difficult and serious feature and is not often attempted. Ascents of the fifth grade of difficulty have to be undertaken at a height of 4000 metres on unreliable rock. The photograph shows the Zermatt guide René Arnold in the act of securing his companion Paul Etter from Walenstadt during the first difficult rope section on the major part of the ascent.

The crowning achievement of a climb up the Matterhorn over the Furggen ridge is to sleep in a tent on the summit. Not that a tent is necessary because of time considerations, but simply from the exhilaration and pleasure of experiencing the majestic silence at night and the magnificent view from this unique vantage point in the late sunset and the dawn. The adjoining pages give a panoramic view from the summit of the Matterhorn from the south-west to the north-east. It was taken at 5.30 a.m. on a September morning. The descent was made along Arête du Lion. Here, just below the summit, Paul Etter is descending by the rope tied to its first anchorage.

Pizzo Barone

Witenwasserenstock

Pizzo Rotondo

Gross Muttenhorn

Blinnenhorn

Pizzo Centrale

Güferhorn

Rheinwaldhorn

Piz Lucendro

Campo Tencia

Opposite page
Above: René Arnold, Paul Etter and the author, wrapped in wadded jackets and sleeping bags, have spent a cold night (−15 °C) sitting on a narrow ridge of rock on the Italian summit. The view is over the Dent d'Hérens towards Mont Blanc. Stars twinkle above the mountains. Large aircraft pass through the skies over the Mont Blanc–Gran Paradiso route like bright stars. A morning stroll over the summit ridge towards the sun, just beginning to rise over the Strahlhorn, warms the bones.
Below: Hard pieces of snow and ice were gathered together to brew the eagerly awaited coffee on the gas cooker.

Right: The descent over the dry rocks of the Italian ridge is eased by means of the fixed rope and the rope ladder. The Jacob's ladder is let down over the vertical crag at a height of 4400 metres.
Without ropes and ladders, the Arête du Lion would be more difficult than the Zmutt ridge. Although these ropes are regularly inspected by the guides of Breuil, the mountaineer should never rely on them blindly. The usual safety precautions must also be taken.

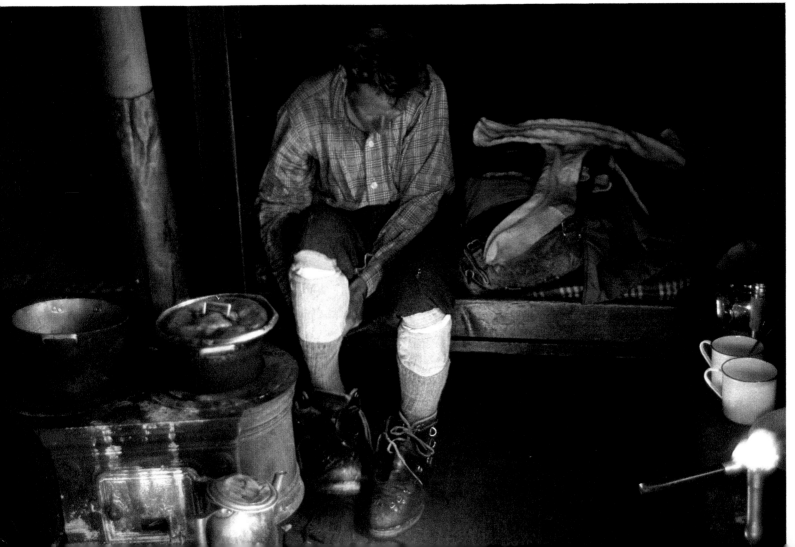

Opposite page
Above: The track from the
Col de Lion (3581 metres)
down to Breuil is at some points
exposed to falling stones.
To the right the rocks of the
Tête de Lion. The south-west
of the Arête du Lion is the
classic route for the ascent from
Breuil. It was first used by the
guides Jean-Antoine Carrel
and Jean Baptiste Bich on
July 17, 1865, three days after
the first ascent of the Hörnli
ridge. The Arête du Lion has
the best rock structure of all the
Matterhorn ridges.
Below: In the Capanna Luigi
Amedeo di Savoia (3835 metres), lofty starting point for
the ascent of the Lion ridge,
the mountain guide René
Arnold takes off his warm
camping clothes.

Left: The small platform under
the icicles was used by Edward
Whymper as his second bivouac
when he attempted to climb
the Lion ridge.
The Dent d'Hérens (4171
metres), in the background,
slopes downwards to a long
and difficult ridge to the Col
Tournanche (3884 metres).
This ridge, one of the most
imposing in the Alps, is 2200
metres long with a height
difference of 687 metres. It was
first climbed on July 30, 1906,
by a party consisting of
V.J.J.Ryan, Jos.Lochmatter
and Franz Lochmatter.

After a day of bad weather in July, the cloud bank lifts for a few minutes. From the Rothorn hut the view is across the *firn* dome of the Untergabelhorn towards the fresh snow on the peak of the Matterhorn. To the left is the Hörnli ridge, on the right the upper section of the Zmutt ridge, and in between a section of the steep north face which was climbed on July 31 and August 1, 1931, by the brothers Franz and Toni Schmid from Munich, as one of the last remaining challenges of the Alps. On February 3, 1962, Hilti von Almen from Lauterbrunnen and Paul Etter from Walenstadt made the first successful winter climb in a dramatic contest with a number of parties from different countries. Walter Bonatti crowned a legendary mountaineering career with a solo winter climb using the direct route up the north face. In four days, from February 18 to 22, 1965, he battled through a new route up the face.

Below: Across the Dom and the Täschhorn a fine display of cirrus clouds is the early morning herald of bad weather. The Dom (4545 metres) on the left is the highest Alpine peak lying wholly in Switzerland. The ascent from Randa over the Festijoch and the upper Hohberg glacier does not present any undue difficulty and can be done on ski in the late spring.
The Täschhorn (4490 metres) is a little lower than its neighbour but has no easy approach. Below right runs the long, difficult south-west ridge, known as the Devil's Ridge.

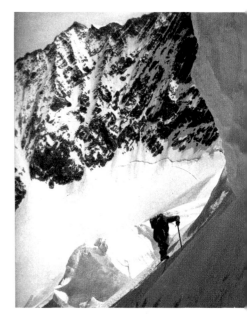

The Dom (4545 metres) is not exactly what is understood by a 4000-er for the skier. This 4000-er does not have a downward run to help the skier making for the valley below. The route from Randa to the Dom hut of the UTO section of the SAC, lying at a height of 2929 metres, is steep and passes over rugged shelves of rock. Nevertheless, the Dom was reached by skiers as early as June 18, 1917. The famous English pioneer of skiing, Arnold Lunn, and the no less famous mountain guide Joseph Knubel, climbed to the top on ski across the Hohberg glacier. For the descent to the Festijoch, they required all of forty minutes. We made the climb in mid-June and had planned it as a ski excursion. But very bad snow conditions made it advisable to make the climb over the Festi ridge. The latter involves a climb through ice and snow, especially in early summer, and can be difficult if the ice is new.

A young eagle in its nest, a few days before making its first flight. The golden eagle (*Aquila chrysaëtos chrysaëtos*) can grow to a length of 80 centimetres with a wing span of between 180 and 220 centimetres. Since December 1952 the golden eagle has been under national protection throughout Switzerland. The number has increased since that date and there is no longer any danger that this most regal of birds will die out. The eagle's hunting ground is very extensive and the injury which it is alleged to do to wild life is very small compared with its value as a guardian of good health.

Carl Stemmler, the leading Swiss authority on eagles, has given evidence in his book *Der Steinadler in den Schweizer Alpen* to prove that the many tales of havoc wrought by the eagle have no relation to the facts.

Expeditions into the high mountains usually mean a very early start. This is for reasons of time and safety. To be awakened just after midnight is nothing unusual. The first hours of the climb up the foothills are often done by the light of lamps fixed to the head. On the lower Theodule Glacier, at the foot of the north-west wall of the Breithorn, the mountain guide René Arnold secures himself with the rope. The stars can still be seen in the cold night sky, but already the sun is rising above Monte Rosa.

The Zermatt Breithorn is the highest and most extensive of all the Breithorns in the Swiss Alps. The ridge that passes through the west summit (4165 metres), the central summit (4160 metres), the east summit (4141 metres) and the Schwarzfluh (4075 metres) extends for 2 ½ kilometres. The first ascent of the Breithorn was made as far back as 1813 from the south side across the Breithorn plateau. The route used by Henry Maynard with Joseph Marie Couttet, Jean Gras, Jean Baptiste and Jean Jacques Erin is the normal one and the easiest climb of any 4000-er. The gentle glaciers and *firns* extending from the Breithorn to the Testa Grigia and the Theodule Pass have become a favourite region for skiers, who can reach them in the spring and summer by means of cable railways and ski-lifts.

The northern face, between the Little Matterhorn and the Schwarztor, is one of the most imposing ice and rock faces of the Alps. It was climbed for the first time on September 3, 1919, by Dietrich von Bethmann-Hollweg with the guides Othmar and Oskar Supersaxo. The second successful ascent was made in 1926 by the famous north-face expert Wilo Welzenbach, with two companions and by a slightly different route.

The route followed by the
author with the guides Paul
Etter and René Arnold in June
1964, through the north-west
face of the Breithorn, was in the
lower section slightly different
from Bethmann-Hollweg's
and Welzenbach's. Instead of
climbing to the right of the big
bastion of rock which is almost
exactly under the fall line from
the summit and over the very
much fissured glacier, this
broad rock ridge was
approached directly from
below. In mountain faces along
which glaciers have moved,
the route followed was very
much subject to the prevailing
conditions.

Left: Paul Etter negotiates an
ice projection. With a pick-
hammer in his right hand and
an ice-axe in his left, he hacks
out the necessary "holds"
while he climbs upwards by
means of his crampon spikes.
Right: The section of the climb
where the rock ridge rises
vertically above the steep wall
of ice.

Opposite page
In the middle section of the
north-west face of the Breithorn, the morning sun throws
into relief the humps and
furrows of the imposing flank.
The Gorner Glacier can be
seen above the crevasse of an
unnamed glacier.

Right: The crevasse forms the
boundary between the self-
propelled glacier and the firm
rock or *firn*. If there is a strong
tendency to thaw, negotiating it
can present difficulty. When
there is no sufficiently firm
snow bridge capable of bearing
a man's weight, time-consuming
manoeuvres may be necessary.
The guide Paul Etter, after
firmly roping himself, tests a
snow bridge over the *bergschrund* dividing the 50-degree
slope of snow and ice of the
Lenz peak from the Hohbaln
glacier.

The route from Saas Fee to the Mischabel hut, lying 3329 metres above sea level, winds up through steep slopes which, in the afternoon, are in the shade. The hut belongs to the Academic Alpine Club, Zürich, but is open to all climbers just as are the SAC huts. It is the starting point for excursions to the Lenzspitze, Dom, Nadelhorn, Hohberghorn, Dürrenhorn and Ulrichshorn. An exceptionally fine tour over the ice in the neighbourhood of the Mischabel hut is the north-east face of the Lenzspitze (4249 metres). It was first carried out on July 7, 1911, by Dietrich von Bethmann-Hollweg with the guides Oskar and Othmar Supersaxo. The smooth face which, from a distance, often glistens like a mirror, is 500 metres high from the *bergschrund* at its base to the summit and has an average incline of 50 to 55 degrees. A very rewarding and objectively safe wall for the ice enthusiast, it had only been climbed five times until 1940, but nowadays is more frequently done by climbers using crampons with front spikes. An enjoyable climax to this excursion is the climb along the ridge from the Lenzspitze summit to the Nadelhorn (4327 metres) whence there is an easy descent to the hut. At the end of the rope, Paul Etter hacks out a foothold. With the help of an ice-screw, a safe anchorage is obtained.

Following double page
View of the top third of the north-east face of the Lenzspitze. Below, left, is the Hohbaln glacier; in the valley (right) lies Saas Fee. Across the Saas valley, from left to right: Fletschhorn (3996 metres), Lagginhorn (4010 metres), Weissmies (4023 metres) and Portjengrat (3653 metres).

The Obergabelhorn (4063 metres) offers the mountaineer many rewarding ascents. *Opposite:* Above the Mountet Glacier a sheer wall of ice rises more than 400 metres, forming the characteristic shape of the mountain seen from the north. To the left, the side of the east-north-east ridge, the normal route from the Zermatt side; to the right, the north-north-west ridge, the normal route from the Mountet hut. The 55-degree north-east slope was first climbed on July 30, 1930, by Rudolf Schwarzgruber and Hans Kiener. The first successful ascent of the mountain was on July 6, 1865, by A. W. Moore and Horace Walker with Jak. Anderegg, over the east face. *Below:* The mountain seen from the Mountet hut. The normal route along the lower section is through the rocky north-north-west flank. To the right, the Arban ridge slopes down to the right.

Bottom: The starting point for the present normal route from Zermatt is now the Rothorn hut (3200 metres) belonging to the Oberaargau Section of the SAC, and in front of which the climbers are sizing up the cloudy skies.

Left: The ascent from the Rothorn hut to the Wellen-kuppe (3903 metres), part of the route for climbing the Obergabelhorn. In the background from left to right: Nadelhorn, Lenzspitze, Dom, Täschhorn and Alphubel. The climb to the Wellenkuppe alone is a modest but gratifying mountain excursion, giving magnificent views of the peaks of Valais.

Opposite: The east-north-east ridge with the Great Gendarme was first climbed on August 1, 1890, by L. Norman-Neruda and Christian Klucker. The passage past the extreme slopes of the Gratturm towards the Wellenkuppe has often given rise to serious difficulties. In 1918, the Zermatt guides' association fixed a permanent rope to the gendarme which has made the ascent very much easier.

The Zinal Rothorn (4221 metres) is a typical rock mountain, formed from rough, firm gneiss. Of all the peaks surrounding Zermatt and Zinal, none is more capable of luring the rock climber than the shapely peak of the Rothorn. The rugged north ridge, which is approached from the Mountet hut, is the route followed by Leslie Stephen and F. C. Craufurd, with the guides Melchior and Jakob Anderegg, when they made the first ascent on August 22, 1864.

Opposite page
From the Grat des Blanc, a knife-edge *firn* leading to the shoulder of the north ridge, the climber has a magnificent view towards the north flanks of the Matterhorn, the Obergabelhorn and the Dent d'Hérens. Directly below the north face of the Matterhorn is the Wellenkuppe *(top)* and on the extreme left, in the foreground, the south-west or Rothorn ridge.

This page
The south-west or Rothorn ridge seen from the Wellenkuppe. Like an imposing staircase, it rises towards the summit (from the bottom left of the photograph). This ridge, first climbed in August 1901 by C. R. Gross, with Rudolf Taugwalder, is undoubtedly one of the most enjoyable climbing excursions in the high mountains. Centre, left, is the upper section of the north ridge with the Grande Bosse.

From Simplon Dorf an ascent
with many variations leads
over the broad Schafalp
Hohsass to the Laggin (or
Laquin) hut (2752 metres).
This hut is a gift from the
Swiss Ladies' Alpine Club to
the SAC. It has room for twelve
persons and is perched on an
offshoot ridge of the Fletschhorn (3996 metres). In the
upper section of the climb of
over four hours, where there
is no track, stone markers
indicate the route. The climb
of the Fletschhorn, just under
4000 metres high, starting
from the light-weight metal
shelter, is a rewarding objective.
The south-east ridge involves
an easy but beautiful climb
of over 1200 metres.

View from the Laggin (Laquin) shelter towards the Gondo gorge. Behind the mountain range in the foreground, to the right of the photograph, runs the Zwischbergen valley with the Camoscellahorn (2610 metres), one of the least known mountain valleys in Switzerland.

On Admiring Mountains

Letter from the Doctor
Konrad Gessner
(1516–1565)
to Jakob Vogel

To the most noble gentleman Jakob Vogel, greetings from Konrad Gessner, the doctor.

So long as God gives me the years to live, my most learned Vogel, I have pledged myself from now onwards to climb several mountains, or at least one of them, each year when the flowers are in bloom, partly to gain more knowledge thereof, partly to give some worthy exercise to the body and to cheer the spirit. What a joy, what a pleasure, for the awakened soul to gaze in admiration at the mountain mass as if one were in a theatre, and to lift one's eyes to the heavens. I cannot explain why it is that, at the sight of these incredible heights, one's whole being trembles as it is gripped by the glorious splendours of creation. Petty beings are they who cannot bring themselves to admire anything, brooding in their retreats and neglecting the mighty display of the universe; as they creep into their holes in winter like the seven sleepers, they have not a thought that the human race is in the world in order to gain from its wonders an understanding of higher things, yes, even of Almighty God Himself. So limited are their powers of perception, that they must, like the swine, always be looking downwards, never looking to the skies, never casting their eyes upwards to the stars. Much good will their contortions in the mud do them as they strive after gain with their slavish toil! Those seeking wisdom will pursue their journey through this world with their bodies and minds ever open to take in whatever this earthly paradise may reveal to them, not the least among them being the stark mountain peaks, with their impregnable slopes, their naked flanks soaring up to the heavens, the forbidding rocks and the cool forest's shade...

I mentioned previously that he must be an enemy of nature who does not consider it worthy to allow himself the profound contemplation of the stately mountains. Truly the summits of high mountains seem to reveal to us that they stand apart from the stresses and strains which are the lot of ordinary mortals, as if they were situated in another world. So different from the effect of the mighty sun, the atmosphere and the winds. The snow remains on them for ever; and the soft delicate substance, disintegrating at the touch of the finger, remains unmoved there under the violence of the sun's rays. Even time fails to move it, as it is constantly freezing to become the hardest block of ice and everlasting crystal... What words of man can describe fully the many species of animal and the upper reaches where they are wont to feed in the mountains? That which nature shows poorly and sparingly in other regions, it demonstrates in rich profusion all over the mountains, assembled in goodly measure, revealing all its riches to our eyes down to the last minute detail.

Thus it is that the mountains awake in us the greatest admiration for all the elements and for the profusion of nature. There it is that a man can understand the enormous grandeur of the earth as nature gradually unfolds itself by giving us a demonstration of its power to raise such a mass, at the same time exercising the tremendous forces pressing downwards. Here are the rich resources of the torrents, sufficient to drown the earth. Many are the lakes which are on the summits as if nature wished to make a pleasurable sport of lifting the waters from the deepest water-holes. For far around one can see the air which is fed and amplified through the unseen evaporation of the mountain waters. Sometimes these are locked up in extensive caves causing the earth to tremble, in some cases continuously. In the mountain there is also fire, producing metals as in a forge. Elsewhere, health-giving hot springs testify to the existence of underground fire, more particularly in many parts of our beloved Switzerland. Sometimes the fire actually bursts forth as with Etna, Vesuvius and in a mountain near Grenoble. In other places where it does not show itself, the fire is buried under the earth's surface. For why do the mountains not fall down of their own accord in the course of the centuries? And why are they not worn away by the storms to which they are continually exposed through rain and the rushing torrent? There is no doubt that the mountains owe their creation and their existence to the effect of fire. For when the fiery mass hidden within the earth is pushed upwards by natural forces, it follows its own course and when it breaks through, however small the aperture, it takes with it great masses of earth.

As it is here that all the powers of the elements and of all nature are combined in one place, it is not to be wondered at that the ancients attributed divine powers to the mountains and made them the habitation of many mountain gods, such as Pan, the faun, the satyr, supposed to have the feet of a goat, who was also called half-goat, goat-feet, ram's-leg, because of the wild mountain country, and since these are the animals whose home is in the mountain crags. This is the god who was thought to inspire terror, for at the contemplation of the forest heights, the heart was seized by an unnatural astonishment beyond anything conceivable at the sight of material things. Above all, Pan is the inhabitant of the heights, the symbol of the universe, whose primitive forces, as I have said, are uniquely shown by the mountains, which lie at their origin, there to exercise their power at its greatest. For this reason, Pan is depicted as crowned with a sprig of fir, since the fir-tree is an expression of the mountains, the forests and power. For his son, they created Bucolion, who started by learning to graze cattle. All the ancient divine rulers of the nymphs are to be found in the distant regions of the mountains, the Oreades, the Alseides, the Heleionomes, the Hydriades, the Krenides, the Epipotamides, the Limnades, the Naiades, the Leimoniades, the Epimelides, the Dryades and the Hamadryades (nymphs of the mountain, grove, marsh, water, spring, river, lake, meadow, peasants and trees). Diana, the hunter, loves the mountains, The muses pass through the twin peaks of Parnassus, the delightful regions of Helicon and the peaks of Ionia and Pirene. There is a germ of reality in them, though they are all myths.

But how do mountain regions come to be so rich in forests? Because they have considerable nourishment, not only from springs, but also heavy rainfall and masses of snow, the last-named being the more effective as it melts gradually and penetrates deeply into the earth instead of tumbling down as a single mass of water all at once in such quantity as could flood the earth and wash it away...

There are many other reasons why the sight of mountains grips me more than any other spectacle, and as our mountains are the highest and, so I hear, the plant life is much more profuse than in other regions, so there comes this eagerness to visit them, to which purpose your friendship invites me...

Farewell.

Zürich, the month of June, in the Year of Grace 1541.

Ricco Bianchi

The Structure of the Alps

1. The Science of Rocks
(Petrography)

For anyone seeking to determine the soundness of a building, the best way is first to study the materials used in its construction. The materials constituting our mountains are formed of various types of rock, and these in turn are formed from minerals. Minerals, however, are the elementary natural matter and the chemical components of the earth's crust.

While constructing tunnels or making petroleum borings it is observed that the temperature increases the further down one penetrates. For every 32 metres of depth, the temperature rises by approximately one degree centigrade. This means that at less than 50 kilometres below the surface it can be assumed that all matter is gaseous or fluid. In fact, the appearance of volcanic eruptions with their discharge of steam and fluid lava are the direct confirmation of this assumption. Indirectly it can be inferred with the highest degree of probability that our world at one time pursued its course through the universe in the form of a fiery ball of gas, just like the sun, and developed into its present condition through a gradual process of cooling. The solid crust of the earth must therefore be a relatively thin covering compared with the earth's radius. And only a small part of this covering is open to our direct observation. Yet what a wealth of different types of rock can be discovered! If we follow the usually accepted classification, going back to the beginning, we first come to the main group of the *magmatic* or *igneous* rocks. These were formed through a cooling down of the magma, which means the molten mass of the earth. Where this cooling process took place gradually at a considerable depth, it formed large, well-shaped crystals. Rocks of this type have a granular structure and are called basic rocks. Examples are: granite, syenite, diorite and gabbro. Where the cooling process was more rapid, the magma solidified more quickly, forming into smaller crystals which distorted each other during the formative stage. A fine-grained basic mass was produced. It may well be that previously a few large crystals solidified within a basic mass as the so-called "intrusives". We then speak of a porphyritic structure, which can be observed in the various types of porphyrites. Where the cooling took place at the earth's surface, the magma often solidified into a "glassy" structure, which means that one cannot distinguish any crystal forms at all (volcanic lava, molten rock). As the alpine regions had only a small volcanic area, rock types of this kind seldom occur there. The spilite and trachyte examples of the Kärpf area of Glarus must be included in this category. However, the majority of rock types of our Alps which developed from the slowly cooling and solidifying magma do not occur unchanged from their original formation. Their changed structure has been due far more to a number of different influences, pressure, temperature, contact with other magma types or movements of the earth's crust. From the magma rock there developed the so-called metamorphosed rock types. A well-known example of this type is gneiss, very widespread in a variety of forms. It is known that these gneiss often developed into granite. The main minerals in granite are felspar, quartz and mica, indiscriminately distributed in the rock. Within gneiss, on the other hand, there is a main strata direction, the foliated mica crystal being particularly predominant. The usual description of the texture (Lat. *textura:* web) is schistose in gneiss, but compact in granite, that is, practically free from hollow spaces. The structure, or development of the minerals, on the contrary, is crystalline in both types. The large majority of "granite" building blocks are in fact metamorphic, or gneiss, types (Ticino granite, Gotthard granite, Andean granite). One often speaks also of "crystalline schists", that is rock types with various crystals mixed with them, but which have a "schistose structure".

Finally we may distinguish a third main group in the form of the so-called "sedimentary" rocks. They arose as a secondary stage from magmatic rocks or crystalline schists. Even while our mountains were being formed, eroding agents were unremittingly at work. In the first place, watercourses, in conjunction with chemical transformations, formed part of the so-called processes of erosion (Lat. *erodere:* to gnaw off). Rock types and minerals were thereby taken into solution and carried away as tiny particles. Where such a dissolving process reached its limit, the particles were once more carried further away (sedimentation). It is in this way that, for example, a calcium crust is formed in water pipes which becomes thicker and thicker until the pipe is completely blocked. When steam locomotives were first used, such layers of fur were greatly feared, as they sometimes led to a boiler explosion. But even in our modern household boilers, the calcium layer has to be removed from time to time where the water has a high calcium content. The limestone mountain ranges were formed in this way in the large ocean areas which at certain times in our earth's history covered the present land surface. If we assume that it takes 7000 years for one metre of calcium rock to be segregated, we can make a rough calculation of the rate of growth of our high alpine limestone mountains that rise to several hundred metres. And similarly we can also imagine how the Dolomite mountains were formed, since the formation of one metre of sandstone, consisting of quartz particles, takes some 1200 years. But by no means all sedimentary rocks are as fine-grained as limestone or dolomite. Larger particles of the rocks carried away reached the ocean regions and were there again solidifed into rock. One example of this type, built up of spherical particles, is the gravelly *Nagelfluh* which can be seen so clearly on the Rigi, the Napf or in Toggenburg. Where the components have sharp, angular edges, the rocks are then called breccias. They appear in the Alps in various formations. An example of the very highly regarded decorative stone is the multi-coloured broken breccia of Arzo in Ticino (marmo d'Arzo). These few explanations from the science of petrography show how much the rocks alone can reveal of the mountain structure and its history. Anyone interested in these subjects should first examine the building material and then the building as a whole!

The mountain clefts reveal a hidden world of magic. Only the eye of the expert, whether professional crystallographer or amateur geologist, can discern these treasures from the outside.

Top: Rock crystal with embodied rutile from the Tavetsch.

Bottom: A group of smaller crystals from the Calfeisen valley.

2. Basic Conception of Tectonics

The term tectonic may be said to be derived from "architectonic" and refers to the structure of the earth's crust in the narrowest sense (Gr. *tektonikos:* pertaining to building). Tectonics, as one of the more recent branches of the science of geology, concerns itself especially with the movement phenomena in the rock covering, and can also be said to mean "science of the movements in the earth's crust".

We can take as our starting point certain fundamental terms from the example of the formation of a sedimentary rock. If some limestone or dolomite rock were to be deposited in the very large basin containing an ocean and left undisturbed where it came to rest, the layers so deposited would all be neatly parallel in a more or less horizontal position. But in our Alps, there is hardly any area where this stratified formation can be observed. What can be seen, again and again, are interruptions and enormous folds. This can only be explained by assuming that the mountain rock covering has been subjected to large-scale upheaval. This idea gave rise to considerable difficulty for earlier generations of geologists, particularly because they were unable to find any explanation of the forces involved or of the mechanism of such movements. Even today we cannot say that there is a finally acceptable explanation. But there have been several hypotheses developed through the centuries which we can accept as a working basis. For example, we have recently been able to define the forces of atomic energy as they are developed from the fission of radioactive substances. But no observer will now question the fact of tectonic movements—the curves, folds and overthrusts are all too visible everywhere in our mountains.

Vertical movements can be classed as risings and fallings of sections of the earth's crust. These must have taken place quite often in the course of the earth's formation. Where, for instance, the raising of an area of ocean led to the flooding of adjoining areas and therefore the beginning of an oceanic phase, it follows quite simply that a corresponding sinking meant the recession of the water mass and thereby to the beginning of a land phase for the areas thus laid dry. These developments have been most clearly illustrated for us by the sedimentary rocks containing fossilised remains of animals and plants. These fossilised remains tell us unmistakably whether the waters concerned were fresh or salt. The whole basin of the Swiss central plain must have passed through a succession of fresh and salt water periods. Sharks' teeth have been found as fossils from the ocean phase, while various types of mussel indicate their fresh-water origin. A rise in the ocean floor opened up a connection with surrounding parts of the ocean, allowing salt water to penetrate; then it fell, the area was isolated, water now flowed in streams from the Alps and the fresh-water period began.

According to the principles of isostasy (study of the degree of a compensating balance between the hard earth's crust and the magma underneath), the rising and falling of particular sections of the earth's crust can be partly explained as compensating movements. It is conceivable that during the geological ages parts of the earth's crust became heavier, causing them gradually to press down upon the soft mass of the

Opposite: Near the village of
Euseigne, at the head of the
Val d'Hérens, is a row of
peculiar marl formations topped
by enormous granite blocks.
The hard granite has protected
the softer rock underneath
from being eroded.

Below: Glacier polishing beside
the Roseg glacier. The glacier
in retreat reveals a section of
the old bed. The rasping effect
of the ice can be clearly seen.

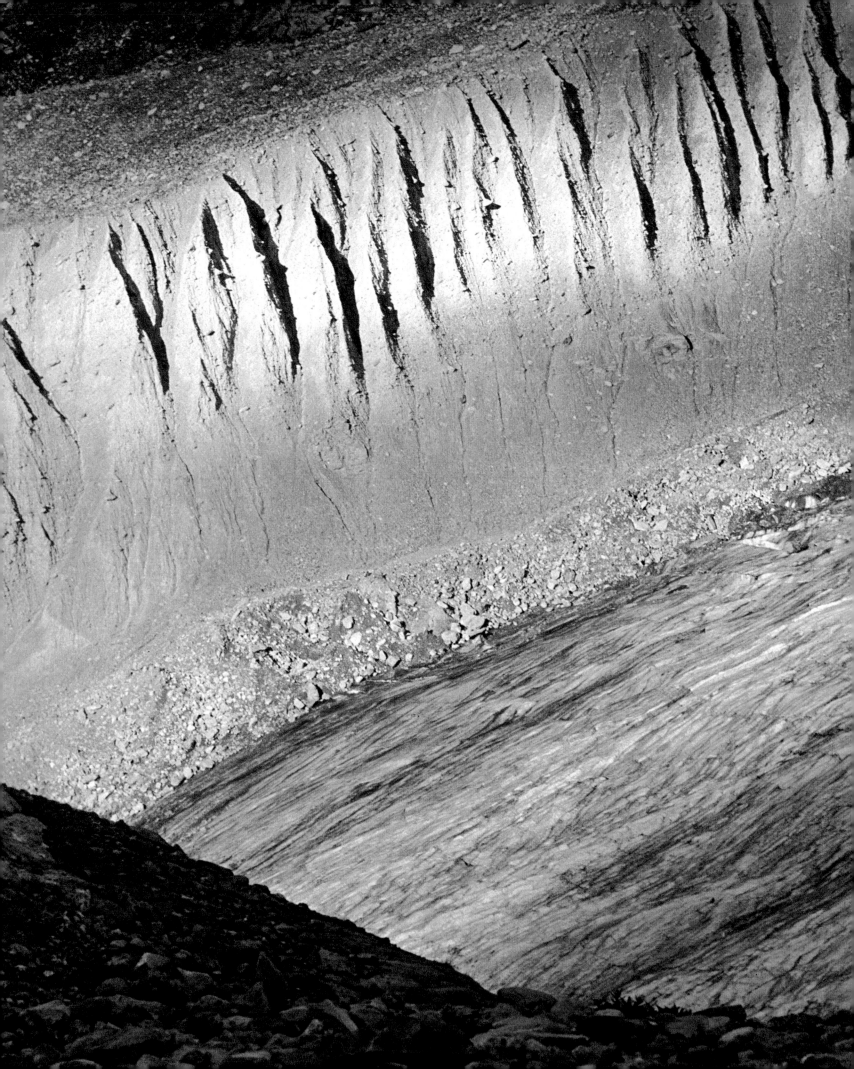

Opposite: The steep slope where the moraine has fallen down from the Tschierva glacier.

Below: Small lakes give a touch of beauty to many of our passes in the high Alps. The Oberalpsee is 1.2 kilometres long. Its clear water is the habitat of the mountain trout.

The Stembach in the Tavetsch. Hundreds of foaming, rippling streams which form so much of the natural wonders revealed to the mountaineer, have been more or less tamed during the last few decades in the course of technical progress. The construction of large reservoirs in the mountains has led to electricity supply authorities tapping the streams in remote mountain valleys, laying pipelines to bring their waters to the reservoirs. Only comparatively recently has it been realised that serious problems arise from this artificial diversion of the natural water supply.

magma and initiating a slow depression movement. Such heavier weight could, for instance, be caused by the deposit of enormous masses of rubble, by the sedimentary rock piling up in the ocean bed or by a thick ice covering. It is already known that the Scandinavian peninsula has risen by about one metre in the course of the last hundred years. This rise can be taken to indicate a compensating movement for the weight removed from the peninsula owing to the melting away of the heavy ice mass. It "lags behind" in time long after the melting process because of the viscosity of supporting magma. According to this conception, the whole alpine chain must have sunk some distance into the magma substratum at the time it was formed by crumping and folding. The peaks have therefore never been much higher than they are today, and the assumption of an alpine ridge of 5000 to 7000 metres had to be revised.

Small-scale depressions are naturally easier for the geologist to survey and evaluate. Where a subsiding movement of this kind in a particular area has no connection with the layers which did not subside, one uses the term warping or flexure. Where the continuous stratum is broken, a rift or fault is formed. A fine example of a rift valley frequently mentioned in geological textbooks is the upper Rhine valley between Basle and Frankfurt. The vertical distance of the break, that is the extent of the depression, lies between 1100 and 5000 metres. This does not correspond, of course, to the difference which can be seen today between the strata which have sunk and those which have not. The former occur in the zone of maximum depression at a depth of 4000 metres! The original trough which was formed was later filled up again mostly by sedimentary material. Possibly the depression took place so slowly that the sinking movement and the crumping compensated each other. The sides of the valley which were not affected by the sinking can be most clearly studied in the south. These are the so-called beds of primary rock of the Black Forest and the Vosges. According to the concepts of isostasy they must have been pushed up on each side of the strata which sank down in the middle.

Faults or whole systems of faults on a small scale can be found everywhere in the Alps. Most of them are also shown in geological maps.

Besides the vertical movement, horizontal movements have also given a distinct shape to the alpine landscape. If pressure is exerted from one side upon a more or less straight horizontal rock layer, the latter can only move upwards or downwards, resulting in curved formations. It may possibly be objected that such folds can be understood when it comes to original half-formed rock, but not where this occurs on hardened sediments of brittle limestone or dolomite bedrock substances. But it is just the limestone layers in the Alps which often display the folds most handsomely (Kreuzgebirge, Jurassic folds, etc.). And one often tends to forget that several million years ago, the layers now to be found near the earth's surface were lying deep down in the earth's interior and have been gradually exposed by the different effects of successive denudations. Given sufficient pressure and high temperature, any material becomes pliable and prone to distortion. Folds shaped like troughs are called syn-clines; hence the appearance of synclinal valleys. Upward folding gave rise to the formation of knolls; known as anticlines. Of course, it frequently happens that whole fold systems developed, and the continuity was partially interrupted by denudation. Here the geologist has to reconstruct them. If one examines the small folds in the crystalline schists, which so often give a shapely appearance to the hills, one frequently finds S-shaped folds. One might well be led to think that in such cases one has come across some folds which have been "tipped over". Such phenomena can also be observed in many places on a large scale, though possibly the trained eye of the geologist has first observed the development correctly and clarified it. A distinction has to be made between the "hanging" fold and the "reclining" fold and the connection between these two is called the intermediate member. In the intermediate member, the strata formation has been reversed because of the 180-degree distortion which means that the more recent layers lie underneath and the older ones uppermost. Where through the application of continuous pressure from one direction such a "tipped" fold has settled in a more or less horizonal position, this is called the cover-ing, as soon as it occurs to any depth. The intermediate member is then rolled out to a considerable distance, becoming crushed in the course of a thrusting movement, and much reduced in size or, perhaps, completely destroyed. It is just in the Alps that a tremendous shifting of whole mountain masses often occurred which were not caused by a folding process of this kind. A well-known and much-studied example of this type occurs in the Glarus Alps region. As far back as 1830, Arnold Escher observed that the peaks of this region were formed over wide distances of old verrucano rock lying on top of much younger sediments. Albert Heim attempted to explain these "inverted strata" in his theory of the "Glarus double folds" since he assumed that the layers became completely folded back, overturning to the north and south. The two heads of the folds would almost have met in the neighbourhood of the Foo pass. The modern explanation assumes a simple transposition of the mass by a powerful thrust from north to south. The mass thrust forward was originally in the form of sedimentary layers lying over the Aar and Gotthard massifs. These were skimmed away from the layers underneath by the Pennine covering thrusting towards the north and carried northwards with it. The route taken by this transposition is, for instance, clearly visible in the neighbourhood of the Segnes pass, where it forms a sharply defined dividing line of light-coloured limestone visible from a considerable distance. This is probably the most impressive example of a major alpine transposition movement in the whole of the alpine region. But the majority of the transposed layers were shifted in the course of successive geological ages, so that today only the old basic rock in the form of verrucano occurs as needle-shaped outliers. In geological terms, outliers are therefore layers of old rock lying on younger layers underneath. A well-known example of this formation is the Mythen, the remains of a so-called outlier covering. The two individually shaped peaks consist of limestone and lie on top of a much younger layer of soft flysch rock.

As a contrast to the outliers, one can consider the "geological window" as it occurs for example in the neighbourhood of Schuls in the lower Engadine. In this case, an old rock covering lies immediately above a younger. Through erosion, the old layers were carried away for some distance, so exposing the younger rocks. (Professor R. Staub used to say in his lectures that there should always be something young looking out of a real window.) In the case of the lower Engadine, these are the "young Grison schists".

The terms "young" and "old" in the geological sense should also be briefly explained. We assume that the crust of our earth has existed for more than two thousand million years. The real crust began with the ancient world (Palaeozoic) about 500 million years ago, and this lasted for 300 million years. Then followed the middle ages of the earth (Mesozoic) for another 140 million years and the modern age (Cenozoic) for about 60 million years. Geological time measurement uses a base unit of one million years for its studies. How petty and unimportant is the brief age of human development against this tremendous time reckoning!

Since the position and course of rock strata are often the only means which enable the geologist to calculate the direction of movement, it is clear that he must start his observations here. He uses the term "lay" of the strata to describe their general geographical direction, and "drop" for their deviation from the horizontal. On geological maps drops are often indicated by degrees of the angle. For instance, the start of a top layer, the so-called core, is indicated in this way to show that the layers are arranged steeply and therefore change from the horizontal to a vertical formation. This does not mean to say we now know with complete accuracy everything about the core zones of our alpine system. The following rule applies to the development in time of a fold or overthrust. The movement is older than the upper layer which has not been shifted and younger than the most recent layer which has. Now that we have spent some time in describing the movement of certain parts of our Alps we must also make brief reference to the remaining sections which have remained in their original position. These are called autochthonic massifs (Gr. *autochthon:* original). Thus, for instance, the major parts of the Bernese and Uri Alps lie within the region of the Aar massif stretching from the region of the Lötschental in Valais for more than a hundred miles to the Brigelserhörner in the Upper Grisons. South of the Rhone– Rhine watershed, approximately between Brig and Ilanz, is to be found the Gotthard massif, including the Gotthard group, the Rotondo group and the Medelser range. Similarly, in the western Alps are Mont Blanc and the Aiguilles Rouges massifs. The material for these mountains consists of primary rock types, especially granite and gneiss, from the Palaeozoic age. Beside these old central massifs, still more recent massifs in the alpine chain have been discovered. For instance there are the volcanic structures of Adamello and Presanella in the Valtellina and the Bergell mountains, with the peaks of the Forno, Albigna and Bondasca regions. The deposit occurred in these cases after the folding of the alpine covering in the Tertiary period, because the erupting mountain melted the upper strata from below. The principal types of basic rock are rough and fine kinds of granite. In the marginal zones some especially fine rock changes (contact metamorphosis) can be observed.

And so in the region of the Swiss Alps we would have as tectonic units the autochthonic massifs on the one hand and the very complex system of overlayers on the other. The latter are classified into:

1. Helvetian and Romanisch overlayers (the northern limestone Alps, the Simmental and Saanen Alps west of Lake Thun).
2. The Pennine overlayers (in general south of the Längstal Rhone–Rhine watershed; the Valais, Ticino and Grisons Alps, and the Niesen flysch).
3. The overlayers of the Eastern Alps (east of a line Chur–Oberhalbstein–Maloja–Chiavenna. In the south bordered by the Valtellina, in the north by a line Rätikon–Arlberg).

And now, having described some elements of tectonics, it remains to conclude this chapter by sketching briefly the history of how our beautiful alpine chain was built up.

The whole range consists of a young folded mountain range, beginning at the Gulf of Genoa, then running northwards to reach its greatest height in the Mont Blanc massif of the Western Alps. Then follows the almost right-angled turn eastwards with a fairly consistant drop in the ranges until they finally terminate near Vienna. The Swiss folded Jura is also described as the "offshoot of the Alps". Simultaneously with the Alps arose also the chain of high folded mountains on the Pacific coasts of North and South America, and in Europe the Carpathians, Apennines and the Balkans. These are described as young mountains, because they were formed mainly in the Tertiary period.

According to generally accepted accounts, there existed at that time an enormous "southern block" (Gondwanaland), formed by the continents of Africa, South America and India. To the north lay the block formed by Europe and Asia (Eurasia). A vast "early mediterranean sea" (Thetys) separated the two blocks. It created the enormous geosynclines in which, through a shifting movement, vast layers of sediment were piled up during the whole Mesozoic period. For reasons which we hitherto have not been able to explain, the southern block now began to move slowly towards the northern block. The Thetys sediments were deposited in folds, pushed over and carried off to the north. The whole of these form the Pennine strata south of the Rhone–Rhine watershed within the region of the Swiss Alps. But the sediments over the Aar–Gotthard massif, too, must have been folded as a result of the continual thrust movement and shifted to the north. They now form the Helvetic layers. And as the highest section of all the alpine upper layers, the layers of the Eastern Alps finally covered over all the existing layers. There are now many divergent theories as to the extent of the "core" regions. Perhaps they have already existed as foothills in Africa, and the Mythen, as remains of the outliers of the eastern Alps, could well be regarded as a piece of Africa in the middle of tiny Switzerland.

Bernese Alps
Valais, North of the Rhone

For twenty centimes the young lady trains the telescope towards the Kleine Scheidegg to experience some of the thrill of the Eiger (3970 metres). For three days a roped party has been waiting to make the ascent up the 1500 metres of the north face. Holiday visitors from all over the world have congregated round the telescope to try to experience some of the nerve-wracking excitement stimulated by newspapers and magazines for many years past. By the time the first party (F. Kasparek, H. Harrer, A. Heckmaier and L. Vörg) had succeeded in this climb on July 21/23, 1938, previous attempts had already claimed nine fatalities.

Now that this fascinating face has been the subject of a winter ascent, a winter *diretissima*, an ascent by a party of ladies and another by a solo climber, it is to be hoped that the publicity for the Eiger will now subside. An ascent of the north face of the Eiger is, as always, a first-class alpine achievement, which is all the more exhilarating the less excitement there is about it.

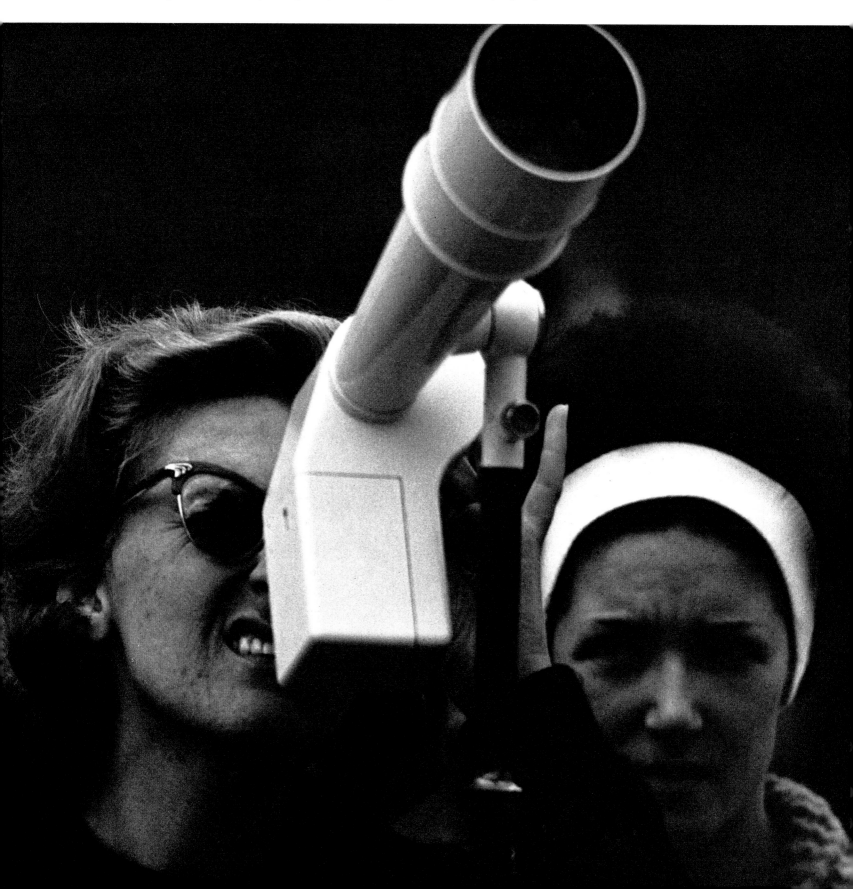

The easiest ascent to the Eiger summit leads over the west flank. This route, followed by the party which made the first ascent in 1858 (Charles Barrington, Christian Almer and Peter Bohren) is quite hazardous in parts and never free from the danger of rock and ice falls.

The north-east or central ridge is considered the most beautiful ascent of the Eiger. In 1885 it was traversed by M. Kuffner with Alexander Burgener, J. M. Biner and A. Kalber-matten on the descent, two days after Alexander Burgener had been forced to abandon his attempted ascent at the great tower. For many years the steep ridge, with its slippery curves, had successfully defied all attempts to scale it. Even those two famous guideless mountaineers, H. Pfann and A. Horeschowsky, had to turn back in July, 1921.

The first successful ascent was made on September 10, 1921, by the Japanese Yuko Maki with the guides Fritz Amatter, Fritz Steuri and Samuel Brawand. This roped party used face-hooks, nail spikes, hammers, drills and a pole five metres long fitted with ice pick and hooks.

The starting point for the Mittellegi ridge is the Mittel-legi hut of the Grindelwald guides association, which stands on the lower part of the ridge *(opposite page, above)*.
To the right of the hut the Schreckhorn (4078 metres) and the Lauteraarhorn (4042 metres) can be seen, two peaks of the best rock, to cross which is a first-class excursion.

Opposite page, below: View from the Mittellegi ridge towards the Wetterhorn (3701 metres). There is a most impressive view to the left from the ridge.
Right: The Aletschhorn (4195 metres) can be seen beyond the two crests of the Mönchsjöcher. To the left is the Trugberg (3932 metres).

Across an almost horizontal *firn* ridge, the mountaineer from the Mittellegi hut can reach the first rock deposits. Seen from the Mittellegi ridge, the Eiger gives an imposing appearance of being a narrow rock. The ascent up the steep slopes can be facilitated by the use of anchored ropes, though this must not be taken to mean that the expedition is to be under-estimated. Over the northern, almost perpendicular 1700-metre wall of the Eiger, the mountaineer reaches the summit with a wonderful view below towards green meadows, dark forests and distant lines of hills. There are few other points in the alpine regions offering such a contrast of high mountains and rolling landscape.

The exceptionally exposed situation of the Eiger is also the reason for the very sudden and much-feared changes in weather conditions.

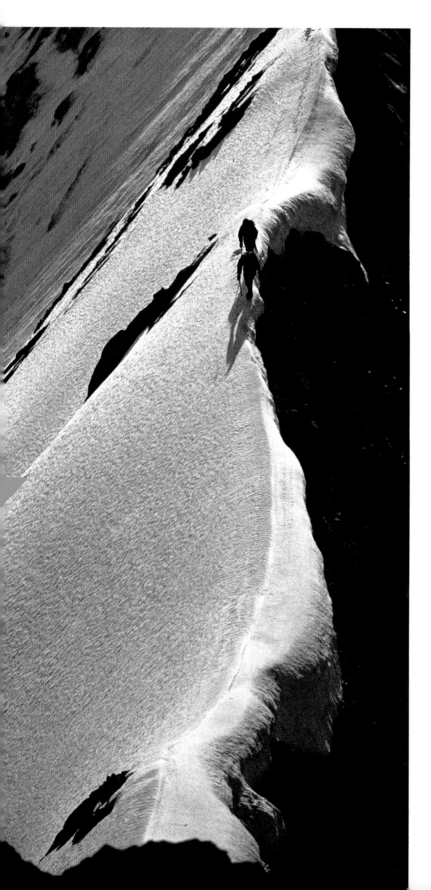

The route from Ausserberg, the sunny village overlooking the inclined tracks of the Lötschberg railway, up to the Baltschieder hermitage right at the back of the Baltschieder valley takes seven hours, but it is never without interest. The way leads at first between the steep sides of a defile along the route used by the elevated water pipelines, one of the famous "bisses" of Valais. Above the Rhone valley, the glacier-topped peaks of the Mischabel group. The Baltschieder refuge, one of the huts belonging to the Blümlisalp section of the SAC, lies at the south base of the Jägihorn (3206 metres) at the centre of a climbing area which is never crowded; it is peculiarly attractive. The main goal of many visitors to the hut is the majestic Bietschhorn, from this side of which are the starting points for the most beautiful ascents.

An original form of alpine
shelter is the Martischüpfe
cave-shelter at the back of the
Baltschieder valley (1937
metres). Shelters of this type were
the regular thing for the first
mountaineers of the eighteenth
and nineteenth century. Even
the mountaineer who can
appreciate the comforts of
sleeping in the warmth of a hut,
sometimes harks back to the
spartan life of the pioneer
alpine explorers.
The Martischüpfe is the best
starting point for climbing the
Stockhorn (3211 metres) over
the north ridge. This long and
difficult ascent has become a
favourite objective in recent
years.
On the last section of the route
to the Baltschieder refuge, it is
necessary to cross a number
of streams flowing from under
the Baltschieder *firn*.

The Bietschhorn (3934 metres) *(left, below)*, like the Eiger and the Fletschhorn, belongs to those peaks just below 4000 metres, but which offer better mountaineering than many of the peaks exceeding that height, because of their position and shape.

The most experienced mountaineers always came back to the Bietschhorn. Leslie Stephen, Jak. and Ant. Siegen and Jos. Ebner succeeded in making the first ascent on August 13, 1859, over the north ridge from the west. The south face was first climbed on September 2, 1884, by Emil and Otto Zsigmondy, Ludwig Purtscheller and Karl Schulz without guides.

The north ridge of the Baltschiederjoch *(opposite)* was first climbed on July 10, 1866, by D. W. Freshfield and C. C. Tucker with François Devouassoud and Fritz von Allmen.

Between August 9 and 11, 1932, W. Stösser and F. Kast reached the south-east ridge, which includes some enormous pinnacles, a very long and extremely difficult performance.

Left, above: Early morning on the long connecting ridge to the Stockhorn. It is still raining. But an hour later the clouds dispersed to reveal the Bietschhorn. The south-east ridge, the east face and the north ridge can be seen.

The crossing between the Wildhorn (3247 metres) and the Wildstrubel (3243 metres) in the western part of the Bernese Alps is a rewarding ski excursion. The long route from Lauenen to Kandersteg over a series of magnificent glaciers, summits and fields of *firn* is especially enjoyable in spring. The ascent from Lauenen to the Geltenalp hut can only be undertaken provided it is absolutely certain that there will be no avalanches. The scenic value of this route to the hut is unique. The Geltenbach tumbles down over enormous rock ledges. At the side of this famous waterfall, known as the Geltenschuss, there are many smaller waterfalls into the romantic rock cauldron which the mountaineer crosses on an incline. At one section of the incline *(left)* a waterfall has presented some problems by having washed away the lower part of the snow.

The broad flat *firn* surface *(opposite)* of the Glacier de la Plaine Morte opens out west of the Wildstrubel. The scenery reminds one of Greenland or Spitzbergen. Various railway projects threaten to upset the peace and undisturbed character of the region. From very early times, there have been various plans for "development" of this glacier world as a tourist attraction. In the SAC Yearbook for 1880 a certain priest, E. Buss, tells of a guide and chamois hunter named 'Kätheköbel' (Jakob Tritten an der Lenk), who was willing to operate summer excursions for visitors by horse-drawn sledges.

The Engelhörner near Meiringen form a comparatively level extension of a lower mountain complex, a northern outfall of the glacier-covered Dossenhorn (3142 metres). They have everything for the mountaineer. The limestone rock forms into pinnacles, walls and ridges, giving the greatest pleasure to the climber. There is a comfortable route from Rosenlaui to the Engelhorn hut, belonging to the Berne Academic Alpine Club, the starting point for most of the excursions up the Engelhörner. The silvery needles reaching up towards the blue skies *(below)* seem to be somewhat less high when seen from Rosenlaui. In contrast, the Klein Wellhorn (2701 metres) lying opposite the Engelhörner, seems enormous *(right)*. To the left of the Wellhorn, the break-up of the Rosenlaui glacier.

The ascent from the Engelhorn hut to the Kleiner Simelistock (2383 metres) consists of a staircase formed by a series of firm rock ledges. Crossing the Kleiner and Grosser Simelistock is a most attractive ascent of medium difficulty. On the south-west side of the Grosser Simelistock (2482 metres) there are sufficient footholds and handgrips for the very exposed section negotiated without ropes.

The very fine shapes caused by erosion make it a pleasure to hold on to the Engelhorn rock.

The west face of the Rosenlauistock (2197 metres) is a fine but
difficult piece of climbing in
excellent rock. The guide,
Paul Etter, is anchoring a rope
to secure himself round a firm
rock projection before pulling
his companion up behind him.
A thorough anchoring technique should be a matter of
course for the mountaineer who
undertakes difficult ascents.
Many a climber owes his life
to adequate securing, and many
accidents have occurred that are
attributable to neglect of
securing methods. If rock projections of this type are lacking,
the securing has to be done by
using rock hooks. From the
summit of the Rosenlauistock
the climb can be continued to
the top of the Tannenspitze
(2255 metres) in rock of
medium difficulty. During the
whole of this ascent, an impressive view can be had down
to the Haslital to the left and
to the Rosenlaui glacier to the
right. In the background the
Wellhorn (3191 metres) and
the Wetterhorn (3701 metres).

Right: Using the rope for descending the Grosser Simeli-stock (2482 metres) to the Simeli valley, the mountaineer has a wonderful view into the depths of the Ichsen valley, that wild, romantic cauldron around which the superb Engelhorn peaks are arranged in a semi-circle. On the opposite side the eastern face of the Kingspitze (2621 metres) rises up vertically as a continuous slab 700 metres high, which is nevertheless one of the most magnificent sections of the Engelhorn for climbing. The direct route was climbed on September 26, 1938, by the Grindelwald guide Hermann Steuri, with Miss Mausy Lüthy and Hans Haidegger with a minimum of technical aids.

Opposite page
View along the Ochsen valley *en route* for the ascent of the north-east face of the King-spitze. At half-past five on a June morning, the top of the Kingspitze summit is shimmering in the sun.

Travelling companions of the mountaineer right up to the highest points of the high mountains are the alpine jackdaws *(Pyrrhocorax graculus)*, also known as snow-crows. Just as the seagulls are at home in the sea, the friendly jackdaws belong to the pinnacles and crevices of the mountain. Their graceful flight always impresses the mountaineer, the elegance of their movements being in contrast to his own. Like all birds of prey, these lively, intelligent and docile birds eat any type of food. Insects are their main food, however. They make their nest in fissures and caves of the most inaccessible rock faces. Although extant in many regions, biologists have been able to learn little about their breeding habits.

Left: In the north face of the Kingspitze. The starting point of a difficult piece of climbing is reached over hard snow and flat rock ledges. The guide, Paul Etter, who is making his preparations for the ascent, has put on a climbing helmet as a protection against falling stones. These climbing helmets, which also afford protection if a roped climber misses his footing, have become quite common during the last few years. Foot slings, climbing hammer, assorted hooks, a piton and two 40-metre ropes form the standard equipment for routes of this difficulty. In the rucksack are first-aid kit, roll-up tent, lengths of cord, change of clothes, food and other small items.

Opposite: A long, perpendicular fissure is a preliminary to an extensive mountain expedition.

Next page
At the top of the face, the climber comes into contact with the sun for the first time. At this bulge, the worst difficulties of the ascent have been sur-mounted.

Ricco Bianchi

Our Alpine Plant World

Vegetation in all its rich variety forms the mantle of our mountains and the theme of many writers. From the start, the alpine pioneers were conscious that plant life formed an important part of their mountain experience. Much of their time was occupied by an intense study of alpine plants—much more than we mountaineers of today generally give to the subject. This is largely because the first alpine explorers came from circles where a good education was normal, so that the excitement of the explorer started with the first excursions, and ascents followed upon what had already been learnt. They sketched and painted, but they also delved into the pleasures of botany. And if, for example, one refers back to the pages of the early yearbooks of the Swiss Alpine Club, one is constantly surprised at and impressed by the enthusiasm of the writers. Moreover, this was long before colour films had been invented and even black-and-white photography was still in its infancy. How much more impressive and sudden it must have been then to experience the alpine flowers in all their riot of colour than to those living in the present age with a surfeit of colour reproduction of all kinds and sizes!

This is no criticism of colour photography, which would in any case be pointless, as no one can hold back the march of progress. But it would be most beneficial if colour photography would also help us to know and understand alpine flora. And this opportunity certainly seems to be given us. If we are happy with something, our interest is at once aroused. We do not merely wish to see, but also to know and understand. The delight of one's own discoveries in the mountains is always the greater and the more valuable as a compensation for the high tempo of our normal activity.

The Forest

If we begin a mountain excursion in the traditional manner, without the help of a car or a mountain railway, in most cases the ascent through the forests is the first stage of our mountain experience. If we start from a low point we shall then pass through the so-called zone of deciduous forest. Within a belt lying between 700 and 1200 metres above sea level, provided there is sufficient water, the beech tree grows to an imposing size. We all can remember the wonderfully soft green of the leafy canopies which appear every spring, sometime in May, or the amazing colours of a beechwood on a golden day in autumn. But for the most part our beechwoods are not pure, but mixed with silver pines. Their large upright cones at the treetop, surrounded by horizontal, shining green needles, may be seen to even better advantage—contrary to the alpine tradition—from the lofty height of a cable car than from the shady woodland path.

In the southern Alps the Spanish chestnut takes the place of the northern beech, giving the landscape its special character. Let us hope that this special attraction of the southern alpine landscape will always remain. In the humid ravines of the deciduous forest, however, springtime brings the meadow-sweet *(Aruncus sylvester)* in all its white beauty and the violet-red butterfly flowers of the spring vetch *(Lathyrus vernus)* droop amongst the sweet-smelling woodruff *(Asperula odorata)*.

In the *föhn* valleys of the central Alps we shall look in vain for deciduous trees. There the rainfall is not sufficient to enable them to grow. Slopes exposed to the warm sunshine and often with poor soil are here covered with areas of Scots fir. Their enormous root development gives them sufficient anchorage and at the same time extracts the maximum amount of nourishment from the damp soil. These resinous-smelling pines with bright red bark on the young trunk, which often excoriates in pieces, can be one of our experiences, especially if in the early spring a dark red carpet of heather *(Erica carnea)* is still spread beneath them. But we also know—especially in the Grisons—of pine forests which are rich in botanical specialities, where the gold of the lady's slipper *(Cypripedium)* gives a vivid colouring and the expert can find the rare insect orchids.

At about 1200 metres, the beech and silver pine give way to the conifer zone, which remains predominant up to approximately 1800 metres. The most typical is the spruce or red pine, the most widespread and important tree of our alpine regions. Its dense foliage cloaks the slopes and clefts, giving the landscape its typical severe character. However, where the heavy snow masses from the spring avalanches break in to the spruce forest, there are scars and gaps in the canopy which heal slowly or sometimes not at all. In the open, the spruce often has thick branches all the way down to its foot and displays a fine pyramid shape. An equally beautiful effect is also given by the storm-swept weather-spruce of the upper regions. In June come the carmine flowering cones which, after successful pollinating and fructifying, form the familiar suspended cones before the end of the year. The pine forest, too, has its own very fine flora. This comprises several species of flowering plants besides the non-flowering mosses, lichens, ferns and mushrooms. Especially noticeable is the common bush-tree of the water-bearing slopes mixed with the blue tints of the alpine milk-lettuce *(Cicerbita alpina)*, the yellow aconite *(Aconitum lycoctonum)* or the large yellowy-white umbelliferous clusters of peucedanum *(Peucedanum ostruthium)*. In many alpine valleys there also grow the large-cupped bright red tiger lily *(Lilium bulbiferum)* or the tall and peculiar turk's cap lily *(Lilium martagon)* in the pine belts, and the foxglove *(Digitalis)* on the sunny side of the track.

Actually every pine forest should merge upwards into the zone of the larch and arolla (or arve). But unfortunately the really beautiful arolla forests have become very infrequent in the Alps. Intensive woodcutting, cattle farming and other causes are responsible. The grand park-like areas, such as can be admired high in the Roseg valley or in the lateral valleys of Valais, form a special alpine world of their own. The soft light green of the larch in summer becomes a flaming yellow in autumn. The arolla, however, provides a contrast with its almost sombre-green covering of needles. Larch and arolla can show very strange tree growths which have survived through many centuries. The expert has little difficulty in distinguishing the arolla from a distance. Mostly the round, bushy tops are easily distinguishable from the sharp points of the pines or spruce. In the course of two years, however, the large blue-green cones appear, which have the edible pine nuts—a special delicacy for the many denizens of the forest. If the spruce and arolla seem to make the alpine valleys sombre or forbidding, the larch woods give them a bright, friendly character. Bright and friendly, too, is the flowering undergrowth, the light colours of countless flowers breaking through the continuous areas of grass. Yellow and red species of clover, orange-red golden hawkweed *(Crepis aurea)* and many other types of hawkweed *(Hieracium)* form with the blue of the violets *(Viola calcarata)* and the alpine forget-me-not *(Myosotis alpestris)* a unique carpet of colour. On the other hand, the alpine clematis *(Clematis alpina)*, as the only alpine liana, creeps elegantly along the branches and lets its grey-blue bells hang down, or the runners of the pretty moss-bell *(Linnaea borealis)* cover the areas of moss, with its forked stem and two little red-and-white flowers shooting up at intervals. In the southern Alps the spruce-arolla zone rises far above the 2000-metre line and gives place gradually to the large bush plants. But as we have already emphasised, this development is not the same everywhere. Over wide areas in the northern Alps the spruce marks the limit of the tree-line, and a thick area of dwarf pine forms the link between the end of the coniferous zone and the actual alpine level. In the western Alps, in the Dauphiné for instance, we even find deciduous types taking the place of the various conifers, and areas of fine birch mark the tree-line in that region. This is possible, of course, in the northern Alps also. Here and there the birch *(Betula pendula)* or the mountain alder *(Alnus viridis)* form the last continuous timber areas and are found at heights over 2000 metres. And many are the times we can find isolated species of deciduous trees in the pine forest itself, such as the white-flowered bird cherry *(Prunus padus)*, the silver poplar *(Populus tremula)* or the mountain ash *(Sorbus aucuparia)*, heavily laden with fruit.

With the end of the pine forest, we pass as a rule into the zone of the large shrubs. We all know the extensive fields of alpenrose *(Rhododendron ferrugineum)* in the northern regions of the Alps. They often spread so widely that pasture land is reduced year by year, and this plant, from the point of view of alpine economics, has become one of the worst of weeds. In such areas, mountaineers are generally both allowed and encouraged to pick the alpenrose liberally in order to bring some pleasure to the valley, but we would not like it to be thought that we are speaking disparagingly of the unique spectacle of a field of alpenrose in full bloom. In the southern Alps where the sunshine is considerably stronger and the ground water reserves often less plentiful, the alpenrose is less at home. In its place we find the dwarf juniper, with its needles always on the defensive. It is better suited to the aridity, is like the alpine rose regarded as a weed, and often reaches to a very high altitude. The well-known juniper berry is really a cone formed from three pods. At first they are green; they then wither away and finally turn blue. The whole process lasts three years, and the three withered threads are also easily apparent in the ripe "berries". The bushes are moreover mostly dioecious, that is the female bush bears only "berries", the male only flowers. Rarer, though fairly frequent on the warm slopes of the valleys of Valais, is the savin *(Juniperus sabina)*. It is poisonous, and the blue-black "berries" are about the size of a pea.

Much more could be said about our mountain forests, their origins and their importance. But in all our mountain regions, men have recognised from the earliest times the prime importance of the forests, bound up as they are with all aspects of daily living. Here we need only mention their functions as wind baffle walls, storm shields and avalanche barriers, and their importance to the water supply and the timber trade. Enlightened legislation and forest conservation laws have ensured that, in Switzerland especially, the exploitation of our forests is carried out for the common good. Let us continue this special care, for the mountain forests form the most precious of our possessions and the greatest source of wealth of our alpine valleys!

Plants and Soil

The further we go from the inhabited areas of our alpine valleys, with their continuous mantle of vegetation, and climb upwards, the more obvious are the changes in soil conditions. In the forest region we seldom find places where the stony ground is exposed. In the real alpine regions, on the other hand, such patches become the more frequent the higher one climbs. The various types of rock in the individual mountain regions can be compared, and the careful observer will soon recognise that there must be a certain connection between the vegetation cover and the rock beneath. As the plants have to obtain the greater part of their nourishment from the ground, it would be all the more surprising if there were no such relationship. But apart from the different types of rock, it is the formation of the topsoil which determines the various types of alpine plants. Every plant seeks to root itself as securely as possible in the ground. For those types of plant which, for example, take root in an uneven rubbish patch, it is much more difficult to establish roots than for plants growing on an even, thick layer of topsoil. They form long, multiple roots, making use of anything available to acquire the most secure anchorage possible. Even a clump of dwarf pine on the steep side of a ravine can show an extraordinarily powerful root formation, thereby making no small contribution to the stability of the uneven slope.

The connection between the chemical composition of the soil and the individual types of plant is much more complex. In this respect, there are many mysteries still to be solved and of others we have obtained only partial knowledge. We shall try now to explain the principal relationships in our Alps as concisely as possible. The following soil types may be classified according to the degree of their acid content:

1. Turk's cap lily
   Lilium martagon
2. Lady's slipper
   Cypripedium calceolus
3. Tiger lily
   Lilium bulbiferum
4. Alpine aster
   Aster alpinus
5. Mountain avens
   Dryas octopetala
6. Cobweb houseleek
   Sempervivum arachnoideum
7. Spotted gentian
   Gentiana punctata
8. Bavarian gentian
   Gentiana bavarica
9. Creeping bennet
   Sieversia reptans
10. Rowan
    Sorbus aucuparia
11. Purple saxifrage
    Saxifraga oppositifolia
12. Alpine columbine
    Aquilegia alpina
13. Edelweiss
    Leontopodium alpinum

1

2

3

4

5

6

7

8

9

10 11

12 13

1. Acid soil   pH content about   4 −6.8
2. Neutral soil   pH content about   6.8−7.2
3. Basic soil   pH content about   7.2−9.5

(The so-called pH value means the negative base-ten logarithm of the H^+ ion concentration, e.g. pH $7 = 10^{-7}$ Mol. H^+/litre.)

Correspondingly we can distinguish plants and groups of plants which are suited to certain types of soil. Thus:

1. Acid-loving: acidophil plants
2. Neutral: neutrophil plants
3. Base-loving: basiphil plants
4. Independent: indifferent plants (in all ranges of pH)

Acid soils form, for example, on a rock underlayer of granite and gneiss, but also where there is ample humidity or a foundation of coarse humus. Thus, the larch-arolla zones with alpenrose are mostly acid, since the needles and leaves which are shed during the heavy rainfall of these areas are dispersed very slowly. Basic soils are formed by erosion of limestone and dolomite, in some cases also of serpentine and schist types. As serpentine rock does not erode easily, formation of soil on this foundation takes a long time, and the plant mantle is correspondingly sparse. The term *Totalp* (dead alp) applied to the extensive serpentine area near Davos, for example, describes these conditions. Most interesting in connection with its flora are, finally, the soils rich in nitrogen. The so-called nitrophil flora *(Lägerflora)*, on the highly fertile soil in the vicinity of alpine shacks and cattle-grazing meadows, is of no value from the point of view of alpine economics, but is mostly so impressive that it is inseparable from the popular picture of cattle grazing on the Alps. Bunched together, standing a metre high, are the shining dark blue flowers of the monkshood *(Aconitum napellus)* as well as the yellow alpine groundsel *(Senecio alpinus)* and the alpine sorrel *(Rumex alpinus)*. If we penetrate the thick growth of these hardy shrubs, we would also find the stinging nettle *(Urtica dioica)* and the prickly thistle *(Cirsium spinosissimum)*. Both these hardy specimens obviously feel quite at home there, while the Good King Henry *(Chenopodium bonus-henricus)* is more likely to be found near the walls of shacks. But if on our last spring ski excursion we pause for a while at the conclusion of the run where the shack stands in the middle of a patch of ground where the snow has recently melted, we shall, of course, see nothing of this grandeur. At most we shall notice a few dead stalks to testify to the summer splendour that has disappeared. But as a substitute for the specimes of the *Lägerflora* the very pretty little goldstern *(Gagea fistulosa)* can be seen. In their thousands, their flowers, resembling the lily, form a riot of golden colour which, together with the soft green of new grass, makes a magnificent transformation from the winter snow scene to the alpine spring.

This is not the place to discuss whether the alpine flora of the basic limestone and dolomite soils are more beautiful and plentiful than those of the acid crystalline soils. Perhaps it is pointless to put such a question in general terms, since in every region a whole group of influences other than the soil are at work, such as exposure, rainfall, ground water content, temperature, etc. An early summer excursion into the Dolomites or the Julian Alps will bring a wonderful, unforgettable impression of this plant kingdom. Catching the eye are the bright red tufts of the dolomite cinquefoil *(Potentilla natida)* and many patches of stone deposit are overgrown with yellow poppy *(Papaver aurantiacum)*. Down from the stony fissures trail the slender ribbons of the rock primrose *(Primula auricula)*, the "aristocrat" of all primrose species, with the same yellow-coloured flowers and their indescribably delicate sweet scent. But the fields of arnica beneath the clumps of larch on the acid soil of the northern alpine landscape make a powerful impression, while the red alpine clover provides a persistent aromatic background. Anyone interested in typical examples of the acidophil and basiphil flora will find a collected assortment in any modern book of alpine flora.

Soil problems are an absorbing subject for research. Over and over again one comes across deviations and exceptions, giving rise to endless questions which still await explanation.

One speaks of "ecologically vicarious" types where closely related species exclude each other on the territory because of their soil requirements. Thus the rust-red alpenrose grows only on acid soil, the hairy alpine rose *(Steinrose)*, on the other hand, only on basic. There is a similar relationship between the hairy primrose *(Primula hirsuta)* and the rock primrose *(Primula auricula)*. Where basic and acid soils are found together, some hybrid varieties may be found. Depending on different characteristics, such cross-breeds or hybrid growths are intermediate forms, or transients of both types. The hybrid of the two types of alpenrose is called *Rhododendron intermedium*, and that of the two primrose types *Primula pubescens*. In contrast to most alpine plants, the *Primula pubescens* should be easy to grow on the lower plains and for this reason become the original of numerous varieties of cultivated primrose.

| Plant Communities | During our alpine excursions we find frequent confirmation of the fact that the association of different types of plant is not a matter of chance. In similar locations, that is in areas lying at the same height, with the same soil and climatic conditions, we find over and over again very similar groups of plants growing together. Such plant conglomerations, with distinct floral composition and more or less the same condi- |

tions of existence, are termed plant communities (*cf*. Braun-Blanquet, 1928). During the last thirty years, the determination of plant communities has become one of the specialised branches of botanical science. It was developed more especially in the alpine regions and energetically fostered. Today the knowledge which has been obtained and recorded has been turned to good account and applied to agriculture and forestry. The standard work on the subject, *Plant Sociology*, by the veteran from the Grisons, Professor J. Braun-Blanquet, of Montpellier and Chur, has already been translated into several languages.

Let us now turn back to the larch-arolla zone already described in order to seek an explanation for some of the basic conceptions. For the most part we find in the wide-spread colonies bathing in the light reflected from the heights the rust-red leaves of the alpenrose *(Rhododendron ferrugineum)*. Here the stone blocks are densely covered with different kinds of moss, and the nordic *linäa* or moss bell *(Linnaea borealis)* thrusts its shoots for many feet across the mossy ground, its forked plants taking root every so often, marked by two pretty bells opening upwards. The bilberry *(Vaccinium myrtillus)*, too, finds very good nourishment in acid soil. The plants mentioned form, together with other types, the family or community of the alpenrose–larch–arolla forest. In the basic soil of a limestone or dolomite region its place is taken by heather–mountain pine forest. As typically associated plants we shall now find the black bearberry *(Arctous alpinus)*, whose leaves turn bright red in autumn, the *Thymelaeaceae* or stone rose *(Daphne striata)* with its elderberry scent, or the dwarf sedge *(Carex humilis)*. The rust-red petals of the alpenrose of the arolla forest, however, are here replaced by the hairy alpenrose.

Even more remarkable may seem the plant communities in the real alpine areas above the tree-line. The last areas of continuous grass in the high alpine regions on acid soil are formed by the crooked sedge *(Carex curvula)*. This easily recognised pseudo-grass is characterised by leaves that curl and bend over in these arid conditions. A colony of these plants *(Curvuletum)* takes on a typically yellow-red-brown colouring towards autumn, so that even from a distance one can distinguish the acid subsoil. In the crooked sedge community we find the yellow anemone, the furry anemone, the spotted gentian, the golden cinquefoil *(Potentilla aurea)*, the grey cross-weed *(Senecio incanus)* as well as the Swiss hawkbit *(Leontodon helveticus)*. As the crooked sedge is also the original plant on the acid soil of our Alps, it is described as a pioneer type and its grass as pioneer grass. Such pioneer varieties improve their growth conditions in the course of time, since their dying plants form a humus. Less robust varieties can thus take root, and the colony gradually changes its character.

In contrast to the crooked sedge meadows on acid soil, on dolomite or limestone there are the tufted sedge colonies. The tufted sedge *(Carex firma)* is a type of pseudo-grass. As it matures, it forms typical flat pads which do not, however, form very deep roots and are therefore often torn away from the subsoil. The grassy leaves are more rigid and are of a darker green. The tufted sedge group is widely prevalent in the high regions up to 2800 metres and flourishes under the most varied conditions of climate and exposure. A characteristic type of the tufted sedge community *(Firmetum)* is the somewhat rare alpine orchid *(Chamorchis alpina)*. Sometimes the edelweiss is to be found in the company of the tufted sedge, together with the alpine aster or the Clusius gentian with the spring gentian. Very frequently the pretty dwarf clump of mountain avens *(Dryas octopetala)* appears as the pioneer of the tufted sedge, or the stunted leaves of the meadow allows its mat of stems and branches to creep over the ground.

And yet another plant community of special interest in our Alps can be described here, the so-called snow valley community. Since the time of Oswald Heer (1836), the snow valley is the term used to describe the gentle slopes or bowl-shaped parts of the high mountain region which are continually saturated by water from the neighbouring areas of snow. The vegetation time of such snow valley communities is markedly short, often no more than three months. The plants must therefore hurry their growth forward so that flower and fruit can reach maturity within the short time available. Nevertheless, the soil in the snow valleys is often quite rich in minerals and humus, and the water supply is always available even though the surface may become dry. It will be understood that under such extreme conditions, annuals cannot grow to their full extent. To the alpine traveller, snow valleys usually appear as patches of dark green or brown-black covering small or quite large areas. The brown-black colour is due to a type of hairy moss *(Polytrichum)*, while the green is often that of the willow-herb *(Salix herbacea)* or a type of lady's mantle *(Alchemilla pentaphylla)*. The stems and branches of the willow-herb are wholly underground, only the small, dark green, often circular leaves pushing through to the surface—an extreme example of adaptation to local circumstances. Furthermore, the plants also appear in the far north, Linnaeus describing them as the "smallest tree in the world". Often very noticeable on the dark moss undergrowth are the contrasting white stars of the two-flowered sandwort *(Arenaria biflora)*, and certainly known to all alpinists are the lilac bells of the lesser soldanella *(Soldanella pusilla)*. The marginal areas of the snow valleys are often covered like a carpet by the full-leaved primrose *(Primula integrifolia)* with its striking red flowers. They are often to be met on limestone and crystalline soils. Most of the snow valley types are, however, either limestone or acid soil types, and the different families are classified accordingly.

The influence of location is also extreme, of course, for rock plant communities such as the primula *(Androsace helvetica)*. On limestone or dolomite rocks this variety frequently forms very large, semicircular firm tufts which can last for fifty or sixty years. The tufted plants generally demonstrate one of the most striking examples of the way our alpine flowers adapt themselves to the conditions of existence in the higher regions. The tufts of the primulas very often lie on the bare, rocky ground. The main root, usually very tough, anchors itself deep down in a cleft in the rock.

From the head of the root, closely packed shoots sprout in all directions. Depending on the ground, the dome of the tuft can extend some way beyond the actual semi-circular form and if it becomes wholly detached, one may even see a tuft completely spherical in shape. In a growth of this kind, however, only the outer leaves are able to survive. Those inside die from lack of penetrating light. But they still remain attached to the stem and form towards the centre of the plant small "columns" of humus matter. Apart from this "self-generating humus" the hollow space in the tuft fills up still further with organic and inorganic matter, so that in time the whole tuft formation acquires an extraordinarily tough texture. The centre sections can be compared to a sponge in their capacity for taking up and storing water. And it is not really surprising that the plant also pushes out actual sucker roots into its self-made food store which gives off water and food to the living plant. This adaptation process, enabling it to thrive on very infertile soil, merits our greatest admiration: a plant which, in an inhospitable rock area subject to extreme temperature changes, makes use of its own decayed humus to overcome the problem of water and food supply.

At flowering time, the surface of the tuft is often thickly covered with pure white flowers, and it is then, to quote the colourful description of Altmeister Schröter, "one of the most fascinating pictures of the bleak, rocky mountains when there comes into view such a miniature garden springing from a cleft in the dead stone".

Also in the Primulaceae family is another rock plant of the limestone and dolomite formation, the blue saxifrage *(Saxifraga caesia)*. J.Braun-Blanquet says about this that it belongs "to those plants which are the best adjusted, most resistant to wind, nestling in the sheltered corners remaining free of snow during the winter, and able to resist the fierce cutting edge of the snowstorm". How can these peculiarities be explained? We must assume that through its roots and with the help of carbon dioxide, the plant dissolves the rich supply of carbonate of lime in the soil and sucks it up. A large part of it is then secreted through the tiny rosette leaves. Further, this forms a thin limestone layer which gives the leaves their blue colouring (hence the name) as well as the power to resist the scraping effect of dust and ice particles blown across by the wind. The leaves also show five to seven tiny so-called limestone-secreting cavities. Under a small magnifying glass they appear as tiny tubercles, but with a stronger glass one can recognise clearly the individual secreted limestone crystals. With a little dilute hydrochloric acid they effervesce and soon disappear. The blue saxifrage is not the only saxifrage in our mountains to show this remarkable lime secretion. As in all such cases, we always come back to the problem of adjustment phenomena, so often discussed, but even today not really satisfactorily explained. For the time being let us just consider it as a miracle—like so much that concerns our alpine flowers—and take good care that in the atomic age we do not wholly lose this feeling of "wonder at the little miracles".

Ricco Bianchi

The Animal World of the Alps

If the plant life of the Alps has been described as the coloured mantle of the mountains, then the hardy animal inhabitants appear to us again and again as most attractive representatives of the real life of the upper regions. This may be partly due to the fact that the influence of man on the animal world is here very much less than in the lowlands, so that animal life is carried on with less disturbance and more naturally than anywhere else in our highly developed country. From this we can understand why the alpine explorer, seeking recreation in nature and landscape, can find in the alpine animals many interesting and beautiful subjects for observation. The occasional visitor from the town, too, will always be struck, especially today, by the animal life of the mountains. How one's feeling of excitement can be aroused at the sight of the great horned steinbock, or a herd of chamois running away or even a few marmots playing together! Of course, the attraction of the unusual may well be the reason for our excitement. If the creatures of our Alps were less shy and allowed themselves to be seen more often, their appearance would become an everyday experience and no longer unusual. And, in fact, there was a time when they were much more numerous and much less shy! Only a few hundred years ago, the bear, wolf, lynx, wild cat and beaver were the most prolific inhabitants of our alpine valleys. And if we go back to the prehistoric times of the Tertiary period, we would discover an almost paradisiac abundance of different varieties of animal in the Alps and their offshoots. The four ice ages which followed brought with them the virtual extinction of animal life in the Alps. The animals were compelled to migrate to the ice-free regions of the lowlands. Since in those areas there were other kinds of animal migrating southwards in advance of the northern ice cap, there must have been in this relatively narrow steppe region an extremely rich variety of animal life. When the ice receded, the sub-alpine regions, and later on the alpine valleys, were repopulated—but now not only by the original alpine varieties but also by immigrants from the south and north, so far as these were able to adjust themselves to alpine conditions. Thus it was that the geological development played a large part in influencing the development of the fauna of our Alps. We have been able to gather extensive information as to the animal life which existed in the Swiss Alps during the last intermediate period from bones found in various caves, particularly in the Wildkirchli grotto of the Säntis and in the Dragon's Hole near Vättis. Along with the cave bear, which predominated, there were also the cave lion, panther and the alpine wolf in the Säntis region. In the Dragon's Hole, at a higher level, however, there are remains of bears, wolves and steinbock, but none of the larger feline species. But even those species of alpine animal which we know today existed at that time.

And once more the northern ice masses pursued their relentless course southwards, and the alpine glaciers flowed from the mountain regions down to the valleys. Certainly only a few types of animal and plant could survive in a few isolated ice-free areas within the Alps. The great majority of the creatures had to migrate and again seek refuge in the ice-free regions of the sub-Alps. And when the temperature rose once more, causing the enormous ice covering to melt, animals and plants had two courses of development: on the one hand, into the alpine valleys as they gradually became free of ice, and on the other hand, towards the north of our continent. Several types of animal in fact went in both directions. And that is why we can find, for instance, the ringed blackbird, white grouse and alpine hare as the so-called relics of the ice age—to mention only a few examples—both in the Alps as well as in the far north.

We would now wish to describe a few examples of the animal life of our mountains. We described the glaciers earlier as forces destructive of animal and plant life. And yet every mountaineer knows that a glacier in the afternoon sun is often frequented by myriads of small creatures. Besides butterflies, various types of beetles and flies, there are even long-legged spiders creeping across the ice, apparently quite at home there. Now these articulated creatures are generally speaking by no means the real inhabitants of glaciers, and only the very great warmth of the sun's rays makes life possible for them. When the sun goes down, the temperature of the atmosphere starts to fall rapidly and therefore to freeze these cold-blooded miniature forms of life. Only a few types are sufficiently robust to withstand the deadly night cold of the glacier. An example will be known, however, to all mountaineers, who go up with their skis at Easter across the glacier, the glacier flea *(Isotoma saltans)*. It is probably the only animal to maintain its life entirely in the *firn* and ice. It is about 2.5 mm. long, with black hair, and frequents the glacier in countless multitudes, especially in May. If we make a close inspection, we will see that this tiny "bundle of life" is capable of making enormous leaps. That is why it is classified among the original spring-tailed animals. If one looks very carefully, one can find on the stomach of the insect a fork-shaped appendage, the prongs of which are used as "jumping sticks". They are placed in front and then stretched suddenly so that the body is pushed upwards. In facing the forbidding cold, our flea (though it is not a real flea in terms of any strict classification) is protected by a thick coat of black hair. This retains an insulating lining of air round the tiny body, thus keeping any loss of body warmth to a minimum. Even so, it is capable of surviving excessive cold without injury, perhaps because of its very small body area.

The question as to how our glacier inhabitants find their food must be answered by the fact that spores, pollen and any other organic windborne particles are eaten. Perhaps in the spring—and that is just the time when the glacier flea population increases so enormously—various kinds of weeds give a rich bill of fare. In any case the adaptation of this tiny creature to conditions which are extremely hostile to life is so perfect that it is difficult to explain this impressive struggle for survival. We can only wonder at it and re-discover something which our technical age has pushed into the background, "the somewhat forgotten respect for life".

There are, however, many alpine animal species which have adjusted themselves to their surroundings. Every mountaineer, during his excursions, must have seen the black, round-tailed alpine salamander. Nearly always it is to be seen only during rain, but then in profusion either on the forest paths or in the alpine meadows up to a height of 3000 metres. With its four short legs, it can only move slowly so that one has ample opportunity to observe it at close quarters. Further, mountaineers do not regard it with any real pleasure—it only appears when there is dampness in the air, and therefore has come to be regarded as a bad weather prophet. The Swiss dialect terms *Wasserpetsch* and *Rägamoli* testify to this. If it were a real amphibian, this alpine salamander should lay its eggs in water, so that they might develop into tiny larvae swimming around, as do those of the frog. But this he does not do. The clutch of approximately thirty eggs is kept in the body of the female for almost twelve months. Only two of them develop into larvae, and possibly these are the only two to fructify. They grow in the mother's body and nourish themselves from the other eggs which in the course of time merge together into a single lump of egg-white. When they are to be born, the young salamanders are already some five centimeters long. Thus they go through the whole larvae development inside the mother's body—and are therefore not in the least tied to the water. In this way they are shielded from the many dangers to which larvae are exposed in water. The drying up of the little ponds during a period of fine weather, which often means the destruction of thousands of other creatures, has no effect on the alpine salamander. Although the birth is restricted to two young animals only and the females do not give birth every year, there are plenty of alpine salamanders. Apparently the young are so well developed by the time of their birth that they are quite well able to withstand the rigours of mountain life. As an example of adjustment to surroundings, reference is often made to the black colour of the salamander (as with other alpine animals), in that black serves to attract the sun's rays more effectively.

It is of special interest to note that the fire salamander of the lowlands, very closely related to the alpine variety, behaves as a normal amphibian, in that it lays its eggs in the water of the larvae freely swimming around. These larvae breathe through gills and in the course of four years become very striking yellow-speckled amphibians. The peculiar skin colouring must be regarded as almost the opposite of a protective covering as it makes its wearer recognisable from a long distance. Here nature apparently took a different course in order to give its creature some protection from its enemies, namely the so-called "terror" colouring. The harsh "war paint", supported still further by the poisonous skin of the salamander, is hardly an encouragement to any predatory animal. If the alpine salamander is induced to lay its eggs in the water at a place where the fire salamander lives, then in fact normal larvae are produced. In the opposite way, it has been found practicable to transfer the fire salamander into the region of the alpine salamander where there is no water and where it has developed its young as if it were a mammal—that is, it has "live births". Is there a more illuminating example of "direct adjustment" to altered circumstances?

For alpine bird life let us take an example from the fowl species, the alpine snow-grouse. Most tourists and mountain explorers must have already made acquaintance with its peculiar "korr-korr" call. Whether they have been able to see this attractive bird is quite another matter. For snow-grouse have a protective plumage colouring both in summer and winter which is so effective that they are difficult to distinguish. In winter they are almost completely white. The black tail feathers are mostly invisible and only the hen has a black stripe running from the beak to the eye. It is therefore practically impossible to distinguish the bird from the white snow landscape against which it sits motionless. They have the habit of making themselves noticeable from a fairly long distance, when they give their warning call and sometimes fly off. They never fly very far, but look for cover somewhere on the ground. Only in flight do they show their black tail feathers. In summer the feathers are speckled grey-brown which is almost the same colouring as the heaps of rock. Now the white feathers are ingeniously concealed as if the birds knew that they could lead to their being discovered. In the autumn, during the changeover period, there is a fair amount of white colour visible. In size it is somewhere between the domestic hen and the pigeon. Feet and toes are thickly feathered, a feature not found in any other type of fowl in the Alps. This protection against cold, however, seems to be also necessary, as it lives in the highest regions of our mountains between approximately 2000 and 3600 metres above sea level.

Here is a short account of an interesting experience with the snow-grouse, which occurred some years ago. One day in February, after a heavy fall of snow, two boys brought me a dead snow-grouse. It was still warm and in its neck there was a cut which was still bleeding. The two boys had been descending on their skis from the Strela Pass to Davos. Suddenly one of them saw that the sharp edge of his ski had struck an animal and injured it. He quickly noticed a white bird which made some convulsive movements and then lay still. Apparently the snow-grouse had allowed itself to be snowed in during the continuous snowfall to wait for better weather while temporarily protected by the covering of snow. This had led to its being run into by the unsuspecting boys and killed. Other alpine fowls take the opportunity of seeking cover beneath the snow. In the course of a ski run, for instance, we have often scared a whole group of heath-cocks from under a mantle of snow. In one case they had dug themselves into the snow for protection against a strong *föhn* gale. In the stomach of the dead snow-grouse we afterwards found about forty tiny snow-white pebbles. Apparently the snow-grouse do the same as our domestic chickens in gobbling up pebbles and using these "millstones" to help digest the hard cornmeal. This is a process which is quite understandable since the beak is incapable of doing the work of our teeth.

157

The use of the winter mantle of snow as a defence against cold gives us perhaps an indication of the way in which our snow-grouse keep warm. Is it not almost a miracle that the bird can survive at all under such low mountain temperatures? With a body temperature of 40°C and an external temperature of 20° below zero, this means a difference of 60°. It is well known that the inhabitants of the far north (Eskimos, Lapps) eat in winter exceptional amounts of fat in order to generate sufficient warmth under similar conditions. Our snow-grouse, however, must survive without food in the bitter cold of the winter storms for a long period. And when they eventually do find it, it may consist only of dried grass, leaves or roots, with which they have to warm their bodies. Of course, the fat reserves built up during the summer can be used up. However, to our way of thinking, the little body of the bird must be a real sorcerer's oven. In surroundings which offer no sustenance for life whatsoever, it still contains life and even zest for life in such a way that those of us who live in all-technical age must be filled with wonder and admiration.

Among the mammals of our Alps the familiar marmot will arouse the most friendly feelings among alpine explorers. Probably one or other observer must have wondered where the strange name *(Murmeltier)* came from. It began with the *Mures alpini* (alpine mouse) of the Roman naturalists, and from that came *Mures montani* (mountain mouse), and from that old High German made the name *Murmenti*, and this finally became *Murmeltier*. The same transformation is seen in the Italian name *marmotta*, or the Rhaeto-romansch term *montanella* and *muntaniala*. From the *Munk* of the people of Glarus and Central Switzerland is derived *munkeln* (secretive) thus describing an animal which is usually shy and frightened. *Mistbelleri* is an old Valais term for "dog".

The animal can weigh as much as ten kilograms. Its close, coarse fur is grey-brown to reddish yellow and corresponds almost exactly with the colouring of the crooked sedge grassland in autumn—a good example of protective colouring. The very small ear muscles are noticeable, possibly a development of the art of living in the confined space of underground burrows. The burrowing marmots work very fast, in that they tear away the soil with the long claws of the front feet and push the excavated material behind them with the hind feet. The compact body, with short neck and broad head, gives on the whole an amusing rather than a bulky appearance. Many of its movements are almost graceful, such as when the young are playing (much as kittens do), whereas the walk of a fully-grown "bear" appears more ponderous. The typical characteristic of the rodents, the gnawing teeth, can reach a length of seven centimetres in the upper jaw and five and a half in the lower! In older animals the front is yellow as only this side of the tooth has an enamel coating. The soft bony substance at the back is gradually worn away as it gnaws while burrowing, so that a sharp enamel edge like a chisel is developed. The typically shrill warning whistle (actually it is not a whistle but a cry formed in the throat) is not given by a designated "sentry"

Opposite: If we are occasionally able to catch a glimpse of the chamois *(Rupicapra rupicapra)* in the Swiss mountains, this is because, although the animal is very shy, one may approach it more closely than the stein-bock, for instance, but also because of the protective regulations enforced from early times. In the Kärpf region, the oldest of the Swiss *Freibergen* (free mountains), the chamois has benefited from game preservation laws since the sixteenth century. Today the Engadine is considered one of the most populated areas in Europe for chamois. The mountaineer who is fortunate enough to observe chamois in their natural, free state, is always impressed with the incredible agility of these creatures. Their muscles are as tough and elastic as steel springs. They make beautiful loops from rock to rock, often across deep clefts, without hesitation, and they display both patience and intelligence when faced with the dangers of the Alps. A long, hard winter can leave many gaps in the chamois herd. Diseases and ill-health are constant threats, and they spread only too quickly. In the last few years the notorious chamois-blindness has made dreadful ravages in a number of chamois reservations.

Right: Weather or umbrella pine. Isolated pines of this type, with branches extending downwards, are very much sought after as shelters and feeding places for the chamois in winter.

Opposite: The fox *(Vulpes vulpes)* is the most well-known and most widespread beast of prey to be found in our mountains. He is found up to heights of over 3000 metres. A fantastic power of adaptation and a wonderful inborn cunning have made it possible for these much-hunted animals to avoid extermination. In the mountains the fox has two or three different lairs in the slopes, at a considerable height. He changes his home according to the feeding ground and the hunting season. As the foremost beast of prey in the Alps, the fox plays a large part in the maintenance of animal life by killing off ill and diseased creatures.

Right: The marmot *(Marmota marmota)* is one of the most lovable inhabitants of the Alps. When he awakes from his six months' hibernation between the middle and end of April, the mating season starts at once. The comical male bear *(top)* waddles over the snow to meet his selected mate.

Marmots at the beginning of October near Wildseeli (Säntis region).

Their stomachs have been crammed full and the cave provided with hay for the long winter sleep. If danger threatens, they give out the famous whistle, which is not really a whistle, but a bark *(lower picture)*, sending the animals scuttling to their retreats.

A deer *(Cervus elaphus)* works his way through the deep snow of the Schraubachtobel in the Prättigau. The stag is the largest animal of our alpine world. He grows to a weight of 180 kilograms. Only a few years ago, the stag was practically extinct in our Alps with the exception of some herds in the canton Grisons. Rigorous protection regulations at the last moment prevented its disappearance. In the area of the National Park, the stag has been able to multiply so satisfactorily, thanks to the complete success of the game laws, that the large herds have now become a menace to the agricultural areas surrounding the Park.

but by the animal which first sees the enemy. The sentries described in many animal stories do not exist as a rule. It is especially birds of prey, even when they are some distance off, which are heralded by this means—proof of very good sight. Unusual and unmoving objects, including for instance a person standing still, is often not even noticed at all, as can be confirmed in several ways. That is also the reason why in recent years conventional and cinematograph cameras can be used in our marmot colonies with very good results, so that we now have excellent well-documented records of these friendly alpine inhabitants.

We referred to the problem of wintering in the Alps when describing the snow-grouse and this is now the place to make the acquaintance of the phenomena of hibernation as a fine example of adjustment to extreme winter conditions. Even without knowledge of the details, the ability to "send oneself to sleep" for the whole of the cold winter of starvation until the warm spring weather comes, has something enticing about it. For our alpine inhabitants it seems to be exactly the ideal solution of the winter problem! It has often been the subject of scientific research—a proof that this "quiet sending oneself to sleep and waking up again" is not really so simple as one is often led to believe. Here we shall confine ourselves to the most important details and briefly explain the results of recent research.

The hibernation period for marmots in the upper mountain regions extends over seven months, for those on the lower regions about six months. It starts when the animals are overcome by a continually growing sleepiness—independently of prevailing weather conditions. During hibernation itself, the sleeping animals wake up about every three weeks to excrete. They all use the same special location within their winter quarters. The body temperature sinks rapidly, adjusting itself until it is almost the same as the external temperature. The favourable range of temperature is between 5° and 10°C. If the temperature is less than 4°C, the animals awake and start to warm themselves by moving their bodies. This acts as a safety measure against freezing to death but up till now no explanation has been found as to how it is started up. When the animal finally awakes, the body temperature rises within a few hours to some 37°C. This means that a lot of energy is used up. One day "awake" during the hibernating period costs the animal as much energy as twenty-nine "sleeping" days. The sleeping itself is a state of lethargy during which the animals are almost insensible to light, injury and other influences. In order to make the surface area as compact as possible, they lie closely packed together, the snout of one into the rear of the next. The "warm-blooded" summer creature has changed into a sleeping poikilotherm, adjusting his body temperature to the external temperature. The vegetarian becomes a "consumer of fat" who, in the course of using up his starvation diet, eats into his reserves of fat, changing them into carbohydrates. About one-fifth of the body weight or about one kilogram is used up. The heart continues to beat between four and six times a minute, and one can observe a breathing movement about every four minutes, whereas when the animal is awake it breathes some 36,000 times a day. The stomach is empty and compressed. The bladder, after slowly filling up, apparently causes the animal to awake occasionally, hence the discharge every three weeks or so.

Various theories have been advanced as to the beginning and end of hibernation. According to recent investigations, processes in the thyroid gland are responsible. It is assumed that during the summer these important hormone glands become increasingly restricted in their movements because of the increasing accumulation of fat. It becomes gradually smaller and hormone production is suspended. The result is a growing sleepiness turning to lethargy. In the course of this research it could actually be proved that during this period of lethargy an animal awoke at once when it was injected with an extract from an active thyroid gland. In spring the gland begins to come into action again which means the end of hibernation. This theory would also explain why marmots, as we have often observed on fine autumn days in the mountains, despite the rich assortment of food around them, have already gone into hibernation instead of leaving their reserves of fat unused. Or why at the other end of the period in spring they often leave their burrows to pass through snow still several feet thick, although there is still no supply of food available, so that then only the store of hay can help them through the worst period of starvation.

There is an interesting observation which Mr B. Schocher has made in connection with hibernation. The author of a well-known and very attractive book about marmots affirmed that in the autumn mountain jackdaws very often gathered in the vicinity of the marmots' lairs and that they were hunting for intestinal worms. Apparently the marmots, which are very much plagued by roundworm and tapeworm, have to rid themselves of these intestinal parasites before going into hibernation, and for this purpose they eat up a fair amount of certain types of moss which acts as a vermicide. The dead worms thus produced become a welcome addition to the food supply of the alpine jackdaws.

We would like to conclude our very short chapter on alpine fauna by saying something about the steinbock. In recent years there have been increasing reports about the appearance of these proud horned beasts in various valleys of our Alps. This is very good news. And for us the reports are all the more attractive as in other directions there is little opportunity to mention positive results of efforts to set up natural parks. The enormous growth of tourism, technical development and commercialisation which characterises our age forms a continual threat to animal and plant life as well as to the beauty of the landscape and rural peace and quiet. So we can rejoice at being able to report for a change the favourable development of replantation, and an increase in the number and security of a species of animal which had become extinct in our part of the world. From remains which have been discovered, it has been proved that in prehistoric times the steinbock was a prolific inhabitant of the

Alps and their offshoots. Up to the fifteenth century also it must have been fairly widely distributed in the region of the Swiss Alps. In the Grisons it was already extinct between 1630 and 1640—and this at a time when the death penalty could be imposed for most crimes! The reason for this was not only the "unbounded enthusiasm for the hunt" on the part of the inhabitants of the Grisons at that period, but far more because almost every part of the animal was considered as having most valuable medicinal powers (it was even considered a remedy for consumption!) A last colony survived in the inaccessible valleys of the Gran Paradiso area of Piedmont in Italy and fortunately came under the protection of the Italian royal family of the period. After 1900 the number of animals had reached 3000, which were guarded by a special force of uniformed gamekeepers. Game laws prohibiting hunting and export were very strictly imposed. But despite this there was a good deal of poaching. Edward Whymper, the first man to climb the Matterhorn, wrote in his *Scrambles Amongst the Alps* that steinbock skins and horns and even live specimens were offered for sale everywhere in the Aosta valley.

In 1869 the Rhaetian section of the SAC made a recommendation that an attempt should be made to reintroduce the steinbock into the Grisons. As there was no pure stock obtainable, some hybrid ibex were purchased and the first herd transferred to the Welschtobel near Arosa. But the hybrid goats gave birth to their young very much earlier than the real wild goats, and hence no young animals could survive. Of course, there were other reasons why the first attempts met with no success. In 1902 renewed efforts were made in St Gallen with another breed. After many difficulties, it was possible in 1906 for the first time to introduce three thoroughbred female mountain specimens from the Gran Paradiso region—though not by legal means. Together with young animals imported later from Italy, they were destined to become the original ancestors of all the herds of steinbock in our country. After successful transfers had been made to the highlands of St Gallen, they were for the first time moved to the National Park in 1920, where they could roam freely. Some of them wandered away and a herd flourished on its own on the Piz Albris near Pontresina, where it was looked after by the gamekeeper Andrea Rauch Sr. Now numbering 700, it is today the largest herd in the Swiss Alps. Nowadays, a large number of bucks and hinds are rounded up each year and transferred to other parts in order to provide some protection against damage to the forests from grazing herds. In the whole area of the Swiss Alps, the number of steinbock bucks and hinds must be around 3700.

A fully-grown steinbock weighs anything up to 100 kilos. The bucks are much more powerful than the hinds. The strong characteristic horns of the buck can measure up to one metre, but those of the hind are only forty centimetres. Anyone having the opportunity to watch these mountain animals going up the slopes will be struck by the skilled climbing ability of quite large and heavy animals. They tackle their ascents deliberately but with calculated balance, whereas the chamois for example always tackles them as quickly as possible with some acrobatic jumping. But jumping is a peculiar feature of the rock animals. Many will have seen in the St Peter and St Paul Zoo of St Gallen how the young of the species will jump on to the keeper's head without a running start and then stand motionless. The horny composition of the hooves is almost like rubber, giving wonderful support on the bare rocks, exactly like the moulded rubber sole of a climbing boot. But the hard edges and points of the hoof make it possible for these inhabitants of the Alps to negotiate quite safely the steep slopes of the *firn* or open patches of grassland. All its movements display the utmost precision and expertise. The shortest approach and the narrowest rock ledge are used, making it seem as if climbing is one of the greatest forms of enjoyment to these inhabitants of the rocks. As Andrea Rauch has written, the steinbock shows the greatest care when negotiating slopes threatened by avalanches.

The "steinbock zone" certainly lies at a higher level than the chamois zone. But frequently, steinbock and chamois may be found grazing peacefully side by side, though grazing areas which are obviously used by large numbers of steinbock are avoided by the chamois. The rock animals feed on all food plants of the alpine region, including lichens. Fescue grass *(Festuca varia)*, which abounds in the southern Alps, is supposed to be the favourite. According to an early theory, its presence must have been a decisive factor whether an area was suitable for grazing or not. This view has since been shown to be fallacious. The water requirement of the animals is relatively low. In winter a change to starvation diet must be the rule as with the majority of our alpine inhabitants. In some herds the animals descend as far as the dwarf pine areas or even lower. We can recall quite well hearing the impressive clash of horns which went on for half an hour in the arolla forest above Pontresina sometime during January and February while doing our military service there during the 'forties. Apparently some Albris steinbock had made their winter quarters there, and these clashes occur not only between rivals during the rutting season but also satisfy the urge to activity and the playful nature of the bucks. The rutting season begins about the end of November and ends early in January. The old "hermit bucks", who for the rest of the year have no desire for "intimate relations", then join the herd. A fierce battle between the bucks is rare, as a seniority system is in force and the young give way without opposition. Where a herd is disturbed, one can often hear a warning whistle resembling the somewhat angry sneeze of a human being. If one approaches the animals, they turn an inquisitive gaze upon the intruder to see who it is and then turn tail in what seems to be a deliberate and well-organised escape movement.

There is much more that could be told about the characteristics and way of living of our rock animals—and there is still much which we do not know. Research workers will find interesting problems waiting to be answered to develop our understanding of these magnificent alpine animals. Better than all reading of reports and the studies of scientific observers, we would submit, are the discoveries one makes for oneself. This is true not only for rock animals, but for all plants and creatures which inhabit our alpine districts. Let us again take to heart that it is the gentle, unhurried excursions into the mountains, the sitting still and watching, the gathering of impressions and allowing them to sink in which will provide such a overflowing wealth of experience. It is the best medicine for nerves overstretched by the hubbub of city life, taking us back to the simple life, away from civilisation and the hectic ways of everyday living. Mountain climbing and nature-watching were indissolubly linked in the age of traditional mountaineering. Let us take heed that this connection does not become completely submerged today in the modern mountaineering age.

(See also our catalogue of alpine animals, page 273.)

The Bernina Group
Ticino
Central Switzerland
The Alps of East Switzerland

In the summer, thousands of sheep climb contentedly to the steep, rocky districts of the Alps, no longer accessible to cattle and cows. The animals are driven into the corrals for examination. In Ticino and Valais these corrals look like prehistoric settlements.

Opposite: To the north-east of Lugano, between the Valle del Frascinoni and Valsoda in Italy, a range of strange-looking pinnacles rises above the extensive forests of chestnut trees: the Denti della Vecchia. The highest point is the Sasso Grande (1491 metres). This small massif makes wonderful climbing territory with a surprisingly large choice of access routes of various degrees of difficulty. None less than the famous Dolomite guide, Emilio Comici, who opened up a new era of mountaineering by climbing the north face of the Grosse Zinne, started his first major climbing expedition on the Sasso Piccolo in April 1935. Since then the region has been well covered, particularly by the Lugano guide, Bruno Primi. Mountaineers from Lecco, too, have opened up some difficult routes, and Cesare Maestri has done a solo performance on the Sasso Palezzo.

Right: The mountaineer is swinging during the descent from a rocky pinnacle overlooking the chestnut forests of the Val Colla. In the distance are the snow-covered peaks of the Central Alps.

Following double page
The haze of a mild day in late autumn hangs over the Malcantone. Extreme left are the Denti della Vecchia. Rising above the mist from left to right can be seen the peaks of Monte Lema (1619 metres), Pne di Breno (1635 metres), Monte Gradiccioli (1935 metres) and Monte Tamaro (1961 metres).

Left: The Chärstelenbach in the Maderaner valley is fed by water melting from the mighty Hüfi *firn*, which lies between the Clariden, Scherhorn and the Düssistock. In the north, the limestone mountains of the Windgälle massif dominate the valley. One of the prettiest light climbing trips from the Windgälle hut is the crossing of the Gwasmet (2841 metres) to the Pucher (2933 metres) which was first performed on July 9, 1905, by H. Escher and F. Weber. The Pucher, like the Grosse Windgälle (3187 metres), falls towards the Schächental as a tremendous wall. Ascents across both these north faces involve very long and arduous work.

Opposite: Both pictures were taken between the Gwasmet and the Pucher.

Above: The Grosser Ruchen (3138 metres), Ruchenfirn and the Kleiner Ruchen (2944 metres) and, in the mists, both Scherhörner peaks (3294 and 3234 metres).

Below: The base of the Grosse Windgälle, showing *(extreme right)* the forbidding sheer drop of the north face, *(left)* the broad gully of the east flank, through which the usual ascent route passes.

Right: Here the Pucher (2933 metres) is seen from the west, an overhanging lump of rock for the adventurous. A narrow chimney is the means of access to the rare atmosphere of the peak. Behind the climber is the Oberalpstock, the highest point of the Alps of eastern Uri. This mountain, 3327 metres high, was first climbed in 1799 by the famous explorer-priest of the mountains, Father Placidus à Spescha from the monastery of Disentis, with Josef Senoner.

Opposite page
Above: The cloud formation above the mountaineering paradise at the Susten pass indicates a sudden change of weather. The jagged edges of the firm bedrock are free of snow early in the summer and can be reached by short ascents from the Susten pass. Left is the Sustenlochspitz. The marked peak jutting up just right of centre of the picture is the Wendenhorn (3023 metres), followed by the Fünffingerstock (2926 metres) and the Grassen (2946 metres).
Below: Signs of *föhn* above the two Mythen peaks. Although they are not very high, these limestone mountains are an impressive feature of Schwyz, as they rise directly from the green uplands.
To the left is the Hagenspitz (1761 metres), followed by the Kleine Mythen (1811 metres) and the Grosse Mythen (1898 metres). Both walkers and climbers are attracted to this little range of mountains, which have an astounding variety of different objectives and a correspondingly large number of different ascents.

Right: The Rigi (1797 metres) still, as always, one of the finest observation points in Switzerland, affords a comprehensive view of the mountain ranges of the Alps and of the uplands of the central plain. To witness the sunrise or sunset on the Rigi, across the fjord landscape of the Lake of Lucerne, is an awe-inspiring spectacle for anyone, including the mountaineer. The cliffs of the Burgenstock are surrounded by a sea of mist.

Opposite: The old monastery village of Engelberg is the starting point for ascents into the Spannort chain *(top)* and the Titlis region. The Gross Spannort (3198 metres) is a rewarding ski tour in spring. The routes for ascending the Spannort chain, looking much like the Dolomites, are unfortunately through somewhat brittle rock.

The Titlis (3239 metres) is the most exciting ski mountain of Central Switzerland *(below)*. The descent to Engelberg covers a difference in height of more than 2000 metres.

"… for such an umbrella causes quite a stir."
In fact it is far superior to any other protection against heavy rain, whether on low ground or in the mountains. Descending from the Grassen (2946 metres).

Right: The airy camping site on the Gross Furkahorn slopes down steeply south-west towards the Goms below, which is still free of snow. Ice-axe, hooks and lumps of rock help to secure the tent against any storm. As the mountaineer will not want to find his shoes frozen stiff the next morning, these are placed in the sleeping bag, but not before the snow has been shaken free from the rubber soles.

Opposite: The circle of peaks of the Central Alps make a particularly beautiful picture in the early morning. An impressive sight is the nearby Galenstock (3583 metres), the southern bastion of a whole range of imposing "Stocks" (Eggstock, Schneestock, Dammastock, Rhonestock, Tiefenstock). All these peaks form the eastern and northern frame of the Rhone glacier. The Galenstock, usually covered for the most part with thick *firn* drifts, can be seen many kilometres away and forms one of the most prominent features of the Central Alps vista (see also the folded panorama photograph on the following pages). It was first climbed in 1845 by the group consisting of E. Desor, D. Dollfuss-Ausset and D. Doll-fuss, with the guides H. Währen, H. Jaun, M. Bannholzer and D. Brigger.

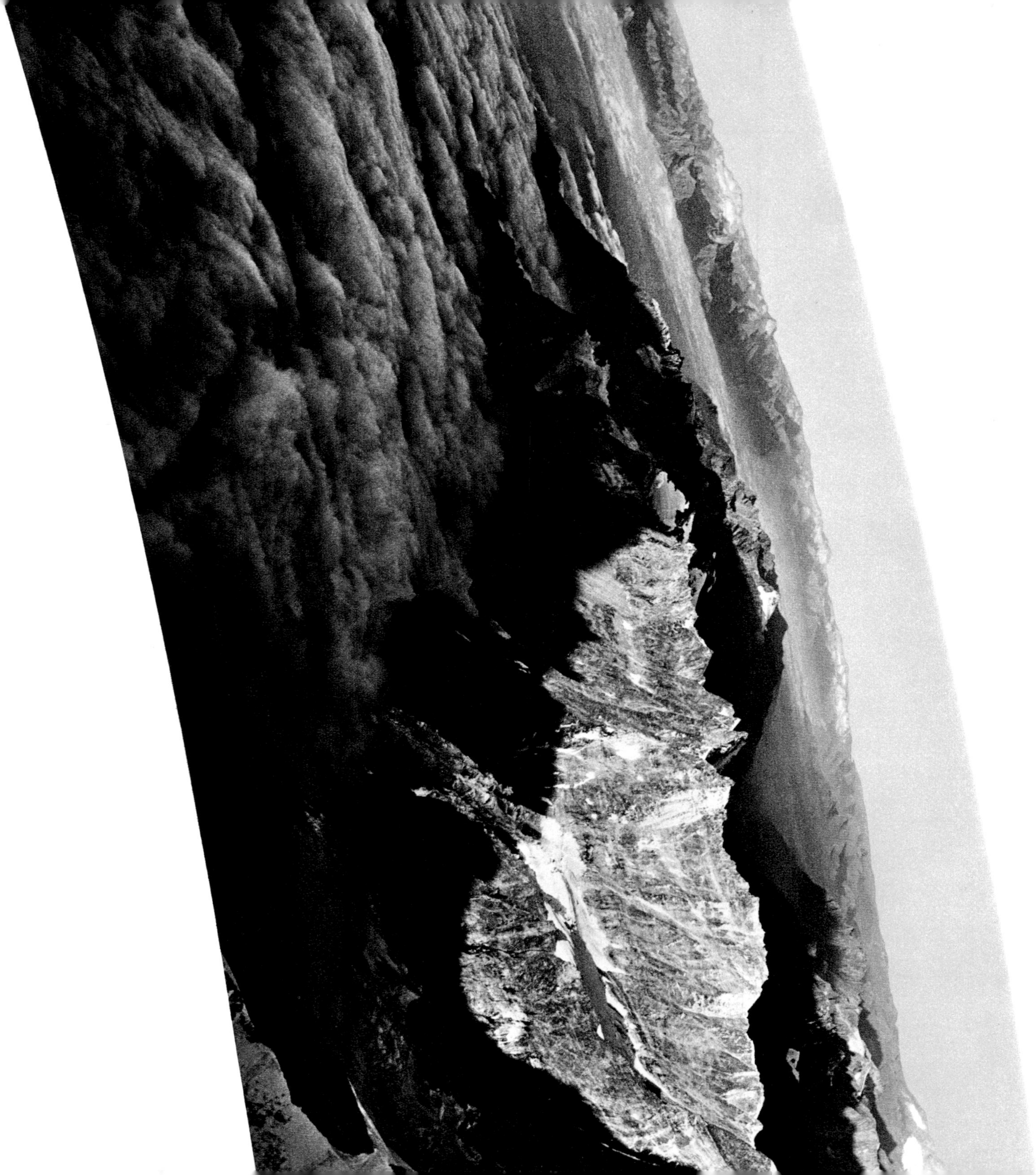

Gran Paradiso

La Grivola

Aiguille de la Grande
Sassière
Becca de Luseney

Testa del Rutor

Les Grandes Murailles

Mont Blanc

Dent d'Hérens

Grand Combin

Mont Blanc de Cheilon

Mont Pleureur

Dents du Midi

Waiting for the sunrise. Gross Furkahorn (3169 metres). End of October. The Furka pass is closed. Snow already lies several metres deep on rock and glacier. A primeval silence descends upon the mountains of Central Switzerland, the venue during the summer of all types of visitors. A small tent gives protection against the intense cold. The cloth flutters in the strong *bise*. The Alps are not as crowded as many people think. Loneliness and adventure are still to be found in the mountains if we look for them. A less famous observation point like the Furkahorn can bring experiences very similar to those found in the course of an expedition to mountain ranges in distant countries.

Balmhorn

Doldenhorn
Obergabelhorn

Blümlisalp

Wellenkuppe

Zinal-Rothorn

Weisshorn

Jungfrau

Mönch

Aletschhorn

Finsteraarhorn

Galenstock

Les Diablerets

Oldenhorn

Dent Blanche

Wildstrubel

Mont Durand

Below: The mountaineer cheers up when he meets animals on his way. The mountains are not merely objectives for the mountaineer, they are part of the landscape well withdrawn from civilisation, offering living space for animals and plants up to incredible heights.

The sturdy creature pictured here met me after I had been camping for the night on the summit of the Bös Fulen (2802 metres) in the Glarus country. In the first rays of the sun we gazed at each other in astonishment near the marker stone. It is the ermine *(Mustela erminea)*, a creature of extraordinary speed and an experienced hunter by day and night, turning completely white in winter and found in the Alps to a height of 3000 metres. His body grows to between 28 and 30 centimetres, his tail to between 9 and 15 centimetres. The ermine, like his little brother, the weasel, feeds mainly on mice, which he can track down in any hole or burrow; he is far superior to any cat in killing them off. *Opposite:* Äsch, in the Schächen valley, with the Stäubi waterfall.

Opposite: In the steep crags of the Eggstock (2445 metres) in the foreground, overlooking the Glarus Braunwald, the edelweiss flourishes in the steep crags. How can the soft white stars of this flower avoid being the symbol of all alpine memories? This humble little flower remains, as always, a compelling attraction, with its fine coat of hair preventing it from becoming dry or frozen. *Below:* The Tödi, 3620 metres, and the highest peak of the Glarus Alps, is a bulky mountain mass. Even on the easiest routes, ascents are exhausting, because of the great difference in height to be covered. The starting point at Linthal itself lies 650 metres high, and the Fridolin hut 2111 metres. The first ascent of the Tödi was made in 1824 by Placidus Curschellas and August Bisquolm from the Grisons side. Ascents over the north ridge, both through the north-east and the north-west face, are very difficult. The rock is mostly fragile and often covered with ice.

The peaks surrounding the deep fissure of the Calfeisen valley in the St Gallen highlands have attracted few visitors from the international mountaineering fraternity. The rock is brittle, and the long schist faces are in many places very tiring to climb. But these mountains have their attractions, too. These lonely peaks are seldom tackled, and in their clefts large herds of chamois can be found. Anyone who is interested not only in climbing, but also in flora, fauna and geology, will find plenty to absorb his interest here.

Opposite, above: From the Sardonna hut of the St Gallen section of the SAC, the mountaineer ascends the Tristelhorn (3114 metres), a lonely peak in the high ridge of the Ringel mountains.

Opposite, below: The Graue Hörner (Pizol 2844 metres) rise up above the morning mists shrouding the Calfeisen valley. Here, in 1911, the first successful re-settlement of the steinbock in Switzerland was made.

Right: From the Ringelspitz (3247 metres) a long, steep, wrinkled *firn* sweeps down to the Calfeisen valley, the Glaser cleft. The horizontal belt in the upper part of the photograph marks the boundary of a famous geological overthrust. The very ancient verrucano lies on top of the younger flysch.

A mountain formation of a
quite unmistakable character
is the Flimserstein (2678 to
2694 metres), source of many
legends. Steep rock falls sur-
round almost the whole of the
broad Flimser Kuhalp.
In the limestone rocks of the
Flimserstein a colony of
steinbock is being propagated,
to the great satisfaction most
of all of the inhabitants of the
Grisons, who are happy to see
the subject of their cantonal
coat of arms once more a
permanent feature of their own
locality.

The Churfirsten chain, for
many years now a main
objective for the skier and
mountain walker, first received
the attention of mountaineers
after the Second World War.
While the seven peaks overlook
the Obertoggenburg mostly as
gentle outspread summits
(*opposite, top*), on the other side
they plunge down to the
Walensee in sheer vertical
walls between 200 and
500 metres high. Climbing
routes have been discovered in
these walls during the last
twenty years, which now form
some of the finest and most
difficult climbing areas in
Switzerland.
The highest and broadest face
of the Churfirsten is that of the
Brisi (2279 metres). With a
height of 500 metres for the
climber to scale, it is almost
of Dolomite proportions
(*opposite, below*). Once, on
January 31, the guide Paul
Etter and the author made the
ascent of this wall. It was a
winter expedition under the
best conditions. From the
Schrina-Hochrugg, the marked
track is followed to the
Palisnideri, a pass in the
Obertoggenburg between Brisi
and Zustoll. Just beneath the
face, the track is left behind
in order to reach the starting
point over some rough, steep
ground.

The rock face rises vertically. A few metres up it begins to bulge outwards a little. The overhang is 25 metres high, and through it Hans Frommenweiler and Franz Bosshard are making the first ascent. A passage had to be hacked out, a difficult piece of mountaineering, before they reached the part where the climb could be continued without obstacles. They would hardly have been able to negotiate this overhanging section without the use of screw hooks, as in most places it is bereft of any natural projections.

But once the hooks are firmly anchored, its negotiation is a question of strength and expertise. The guide Paul Etter has both. He pulls himself upwards with a swing, leaving me with the impression that it is all really no more than an average gymnastic exercise.

After the overhang has been successfully left behind, making full use of the rope, the south face of the Brisi offers an abundant variety of fine and difficult climbing. A few rope-lengths beneath the summit, near an enclosed "chimney", a record book has been placed. In it have been recorded the not very many ascents of this difficult climbing area. Several times I came across the name Geny Steiger. This outstanding mountain guide from Walenstadt, together with his wife Gaby, has probably made the greatest number of first ascents of the Churfirsten faces.

We were very fortunate to have selected a sunny day which concluded a long period of fine weather. As soon as we reached the summit it started to snow. We made the descent over the Selamatt Alp through deep powdery snow to Alt St Johann.

Before starting to drop down towards Lake Constance, the Alps of north-east Switzerland form a picturesque feature of a very special type in the Säntis region. Viewed from the north, the Säntis (2501 metres), with its two fields of *firn*, Grosse Schnee and Blaue Schnee, giving the mountain its eternal snow, forms the central feature of a range of symmetrical shape. The Säntis region, called by its admirers the Alpstein, consists of three parallel mountain ranges, originating from a central axis, Säntis–Altmann–Mutscher. Between the limestone rock of the somewhat strange-looking summits, there are alpine meadows and lakes. The bottom photograph on this page shows the Alpli, and the one opposite is of the Fählensee.

Opposite, above: The eight Kreuzberge form a jagged mountain chain, from the pinnacles of which the mountaineer obtains some wonderful views down to the Rhine valley. For the most part the rock is excellent. It is therefore not surprising that in this limited area there is a rich variety of climbing routes, from the easiest ascent, the third grade through the west fissure, to the very difficult routes of some of the north and south faces.

Opposite, below: The central chain, between Altmann and Widderalpstöcken, offers a number of splendid rock excursions.

The Rotturm also involves a difficult ascent, even on the easiest route. Over its south plateau there is an ascent of the sixth grade of difficulty. The peak of the Hundstein, which can be reached by a track from the east, presents itself from the south as an imposing bastion, the routes over which have some extremely difficult sections.

Right: Steinbock with its winter fur in the rocks of the Wildhuser Schafberg.

The steinbock (Capra ibex), which appears in the arms of the canton of the Grisons and for many people is the symbol of all alpine animals, had become extinct in the Swiss Alps by 1850. Superstition and the ease of hunting it down were both responsible for the disappearance of this imposing mountain animal.

Thanks to the efforts of many nature lovers, it was possible, after abortive earlier attempts, to introduce some new herds. In 1911 some selected animals were taken from the St Peter and St Paul nature reserve at St Gallen and transferred to form what is now the oldest steinbock colony in Switzerland in the Graue Hörner of the St Gallen highlands. The St Gallen steinbock are descended from the region of the Gran Paradiso, now the Italian National Park and a former royal hunting ground, where the steinbock had survived, thanks to rigorously enforced game laws. Today, some 4000 of these animals live in forty herds, more than 700 of them in the Piz Albris (Engadine) alone. Steinbock are inhabitants of the mountain and can climb to heights of up to 3500 metres. They are ruminants whose food is entirely vegetarian.

The photographs on these pages were taken at the Wildhuser Schafberg. With the exception of the two pictures showing the mother with calf and an old stag during moulting, all the others were taken in November. Bucks, roes and their young congregate in winter quarters on the slope facing south. A fine supply of fat protects the animals from the rigours of the long winter in the mountains. A fully grown buck, weighing 100 kilos in all, can carry as much as 35 kilos of fat on him. After the rigours of winter, the steinbock often has a miserable appearance by the time spring comes round. But this, however, is due more to moulting than to any sign of bad health. Now the bucks leave their hinds, who produce their young at the end of May or beginning of June. Only a few hours afterwards, the latter are able to follow their mother into the steep slopes of the countryside.

Opposite: View from the fourth Kreuzberg (2059 metres) of the Säntis region to the west face of the third Kreuzberg (2020 metres). The normal route for ascents lies through the deepest fault *(left)* of this geological spectacle, which at the same time is the easiest climbing route in the whole Kreuzbergen (Grade I). The rib, almost exactly along the fall line from the summit, offers a fine ascent of medium difficulty (Grade III).

Left: The feats of mountaineering performed by outstanding lady mountaineers like Loulou Boulaz or Yvette Vaucher have long shown that mountaineering is by no means exclusively a man's sport. But even those ladies who would not feel inclined to turn their hand at tackling the major faces of the Alps can have just as much fun in climbing as they do in swimming or tennis. Part of the normal ascent route to the Scherenspitz (1926 metres) in the western part of the Säntis region.

Following double page
The central Rätikon with Drusenfluh, Sulzfluh and Scheienfluh is a limestone climbing area of Dolomite proportions.
Left: The indented south-east face of the Kleiner Drusenturm (Dietrich / Maeder route).
Right, above: Kleiner Drusenturm (2754 metres) from the north-east.
Right, below: Sulzfluh (2817 metres) from the south. In the left half of the face are the routes running from left to right known as the "Neumann / Stanek", the "Direct" and the "Austriaken fissure".

Some of the finest alpine summits are to be found in the Bernina group. The glaciation is very heavy, and the shape of the mountains is desolate and rugged. The highest point is the Piz Bernina (4049 metres), the last of the peaks over 4000 metres of the eastern Alps. It was first climbed on September 13, 1850, by Johann Coaz with Jon and Lorenz Ragut Tscharner over the east ridge.

Opposite, above: Photograph taken with the telelens of the Bernina group from Las Trais Fluors (V. Saluver). From left to right, the Bellavista (3922 metres), the Piz Zupò (3995 metres), Piz Morteratsch (3751 metres), Piz Bernina, Piz Scerscen (3971 metres), Piz Roseg (3920 metres).

Opposite, below: The finest ridge of the Bernina and one of the most beautiful of the whole Alps is the Crast'Alva (Bianco-grat). From the Tschierva hut, the track leads over the Tschierva glacier and over steep overhanging *firn* to the Fuorcla Prievlusa, the deepest depression between the Piz Bernina and Piz Morteratsch. The view looks across to the Piz Palü (3905 metres) the three prominent north face ridges of which can be clearly seen in profile, to the Bellavista and to Piz Zupò.
Right: On the Fuorcla Prievlusa crampons are usually taken off as there now follows a climbing section over rock right up to the beginning of the big *firn* ridge.

Over the Prievlus rocks the peculiar shape of the *firn* edge of the Crast'Alva runs in an almost exactly north-south direction. Given good conditions, it is an unforgettable experience to climb along it *(right)*.

The *firn* ridge does not end at the Bernina, but on the Piz Alv (3995 metres), an offshoot peak which is separated from the Bernina summit by a fissure. The crossing of this fissure is often the most difficult part of the ascent.

Opposite: View of the fissure. What looks like a lower rock peak on the left is, in fact, the Bernina summit.

The crossing of the Bernina via the Crast'Alva and Spalla ridge involves a route running in a straight line north to south along the whole mountain. Paul Güssfeld led the first ascent of the Crast'Alva with Hans Grass and Johann Gross on August 12, 1878.

From the north-west the Piz Palü is a mountain of fascinating beauty. Three pillars of rock split the huge overhanging glacier, giving the mountain a symmetrical structure. The east summit, lying entirely on Swiss territory and the easiest to climb, is 3882 metres high. The centre summit, which can be reached from the east summit across a very much fissured ridge, often subject to snowdrifts, is 3905 metres high, the west summit, or Piz Spinas, 3823 metres. The crossing of the three peaks is a rewarding, not too difficult excursion for the experienced mountaineer. The routes over the north face pillar are all exciting ascents partly of great difficulty. The east summit was probably first climbed on August 12, 1835, by Oswald Heer, Meuli and P. Flury with Johann Machutz and the famous chamois hunter Gion Marchet Colani ("King of the Bernina").

Left: Ascending the east summit of the Piz Palü.

Opposite: The guide Erich Haltiner leaps a crevasse in the Pers glacier. To leap across so wide a crevasse demands courage and expertise. In practice such leaps are seldom necessary, and then usually only when crossing deep fissures during the descent.

Opposite: The east summit of Piz Palü (3882 metres) from the east. Across the ridge *(left)* the normal route runs from the shoulder. The ridge to the right is the upper section of the eastern rib of the north face, which was climbed on August 22, 1899, by Moritz Kuffner with Martin Schocher and Alexander Burgener.

Right: In the western section of the Bernina group, beside the fissured Roseg glacier, on the "Plattas" rock, lies the Coaz hut of the Rhaetia section of the SAC. The modern sixteen-sided hut is the work of the well-known designer of huts Jakob Eschenmoser, who before this pioneered a new design in the construction of the Dom hut.

Right, above: View out to the Roseg valley.

Right, below: Evening sun on the Coaz hut, in the background the break-up of the Roseg glacier.

"Oh for the free life of the Alps" are the opening words of a popular folk-song. The life of the alpine shepherd—once the symbol of the Swiss way of life—is not the attraction it used to be. Mountain co-operative societies and private farmers have the utmost difficulty in finding anyone to look after their fields. The life of the alpine farmer is hard and not very remunerative. There are many small alpine meadows which have fallen into disuse because there are no herdsmen to look after them. Moving the cattle up to the higher pastures in the summer is still an important function on the farm.

Herbert Maeder

On Becoming a Mountaineer

The alpine chain extends through Switzerland from west to east. There is no high point in this small country from which, given clear weather, it is impossible to see mountains. From the long line of the Jura heights, the view stretches south-eastwards, over the villages and towns of the central region, to where it meets the rugged outline of the alpine chain glittering with snow. Numerous, too, are the viewpoints to the north, east and south of Switzerland, as numerous as the inns that take their names from their elevated location. Who has not encountered those many places called *Alpenblick, Bellevue, Rigiblick, Säntisblick, Jungfraublick* (alpine view, splendid view, Rigi view, Säntis view, Jungfrau view)? Whether or not he only knows the Weissenstein, Uetliberg, Randen, Irchel or Seerücken, the Swiss who does not grow up in the mountains at any rate grows up within sight of them. As a child his interest is aroused by the mountain ranges which in high summer are still covered in ice and snow. Panoramas which are to be found at many observation points give the names of the numerous peaks. Many of them are odd, many poetical, to stimulate the child's imagination.

School excursions or family outings sooner or later lead to the foothills of the Alps, those hills that lie in front of the high mountains and are free of snow in the summer, and bring the whole fantastic panorama of the mountains into focus. From the depths of the valley, narrow paths struggle upwards through wooded slopes to the high meadows where the alpine people graze their cattle, and there the children raise their first shouts of joy as the mountain air brings to them new zest for living. If the trip does not end at the high meadow, if a real peak is surmounted, with a cairn or some other symbol to mark the actual summit, then enthusiasm knows no bounds. The eye is led down to the valley, and out to the central plain. Perhaps one can distinguish the steeple of one's own village church or the street pattern of the town. The circle is complete. After seeing many times the view up to the hills that arouses the urge to climb them, there follows the view out into the wide world beyond.

If the trips into the mountains are planned so as to be within the capacity of the children taking part, then parents and teachers can be assured of the excited response of their charges. I believe that all children are mountain enthusiasts. On many occasions I have taken my own and other children for such excursions, and always their enthusiasm has been a gratifying, recurring pleasure. Children experience the world of mountains in the way adults should do, relaxed, living for each moment and each new pleasure: the cool stream which can be turned into a miniature lake with the help of a few stones, the slab of rock that asks to be climbed and from which one can run down so wonderfully, the cattle in the fields that pass their rough tongues over the arms of the boys and girls, the colourful flowers so different from those of the valley, not to mention the piece of snow which has survived the summer in the shadow of a rock. The daily timetable of lessons is forgotten, there is no ambitious objective—they are just there to enjoy themselves, where everything is beautiful and different.

225

But there are adults, parents as well as school teachers, who, having left their world of childhood for ever, have no feeling for the poetry of the mountains and lay down an objective for their charges. I have even seen classes being marched, almost with military precision, perspiring and spluttering, to reach the goal set for the day. Poor children, poor adults! No time for playing games, picking flowers, admiring trees and animals. With blisters swelling on feet unused to such marches, they arrive in the evening at the shelter or mountain inn completely exhausted, the proud father or teacher at the head. This is not the way to do it; this only results in the children being sluggish because their strength has been overtaxed. Pleasure is stifled. The impression of the mountains becomes a nightmare. Mountain trips by the whole class can be a good thing, kindling the fire of enthusiasm in these young people, to make them eventually into mountaineers. But it requires guidance from someone who is familiar with the mountains and who knows what the children, down to the least robust of the party, are able to accomplish.

When anyone takes young people or children into the mountains either for summer walking or winter skiing, he assumes a heavy responsibility. The tragic story of repeated accidents is sad evidence of the fact that many teachers, clergymen and other youth leaders have little idea of what is entailed.

Anyone seeing how school groups take part enthusiastically in mountain rambles might be led to believe that the Swiss are a nation of mountaineers. They are not. Perhaps, rather, a nation of mountain travellers? In fact, the increasing network of mountain railways carries not only foreign tourists to the peaks and slopes, but even more the descendants of that nation of peasants which existed before the greater peaks were "civilised" in this fashion. Nevertheless, it should be said that not only do the cable railways enjoy a rich tourist traffic, but even more so do the mountain inns and shelters which are reached only on foot, and are crowded in the high season.

When primary school days are over and further study and training prepare the younger generation for their careers, how does one become a member of that fraternity of "conquerors of the useless", as that great French alpinist Lionel Terray once so accurately described the mountaineer?

Quite simply: one climbs mountains whenever the opportunity presents itself and against every conceivable obstacle. Thirst for adventure and longing for distant parts fill one's thoughts; walking, one falls in love with the heights, but then one finds oneself wanting to leave the well-known track and move closer to the steep, forbidding peaks which until then have been a limitation to a walking trip. One seeks the experience of meeting nature face to face.

The desire to climb difficult peaks brings problems for young people and their families. It may be the aspirant's luck to have a father who is an experienced climber, and who can advise his son or daughter in the mental approach and techniques of mountaineering. But it would certainly be very unfortunate if parents were to oppose their children's mountain dreams. I agree with their feelings of anxiety, but I usually find that their objections generate exactly the opposite of what they expected. There are, however, various possibilities. The Swiss Alpine Club, through their youth section, endeavours to give guidance and instruction to the young climber. Boys, and in many places girls as well, who are at least fifteen years old, can join excursions and courses where they obtain instruction from experienced climbers. In the Club huts the young people enjoy the same reductions as full members.

There are a number of climbing schools, the best known of which is near Meiringen, run by Arnold Glatthard, a guide from the Bernese Oberland, which offer courses on rock and ice. Basic military training also includes a one-week period of instruction. Anyone who knows an experienced climber and who can join him on a first trip, is especially fortunate.

On many of our excursions into the foothills of the Alps, my parents fired me with enthusiasm for mountaineering. From the peaks of the Säntis region, whose stark silhouette threads the green range of hills of the Appenzell and Toggenburg country, I had my first views of the mountain ranges of the Alps. From my home in Wil, the Säntis seemed to be the highest mountain in the world, but even as a boy I saw that to the south, east and west there were innumerable other peaks rising up one behind the other, wide expanses covered with ice, but also dark pinnacles among them, and I saw that many of them were far higher than the Säntis. The desire to know these peaks more intimately became the more compelling as I grew older. It was a book I came across accidentally that set me off on my first Alpine trip: it was Louis Trenker's *My Mountains*. The pictures in this book showed me all that was involved in climbing mountains. Climbers clinging to vertical rock faces appeared as black silhouettes squeezed into narrow fissures. Ice splinters poured down through the dark sky as the heavy axes did their work, and skiers laid their trails across white slopes and hollows. These reproductions of the wonderful world of the mountaineer excited me so much that I had only one wish: to get to know the reality of everything described in it.

A neighbour I had never thought of as a mountaineer, as he bore little resemblance to Louis Trenker with his smoking pipe and flabby hat, nevertheless turned out to be quite an experienced alpinist. He took me into the mountains when I was sixteen. Our first trip was to the Glärnisch. Normally this is not a difficult mountain by any means, yet quite strenuous as a day trip from Wil, and we did not make it any easier by climbing the Ruchen-Glärnisch, the Vrenelisgärtli and the Bächistock. There was little climbing as such, but the road was long and taxed our strength to the utmost. There was a small glacier to cross which, as is usually the case in autumn, was severely fissured. Endurance, sure footing and a general ability for real mountain climbing could thus be tested. It is on similar preliminary trips that the mountain guides of the classic age used to try out their clients before undertaking difficult excursions with them. And still today no guide with any feeling of responsibility would ever take a newcomer straight out on to an extensive tour. The experienced mountaineer soon discovers in the course of such "aptitude tests" the calibre of his charges. Right at the start, when leaving the valley, which usually means taking a path leading to the hut, the highest point of the trip, he watches his charges and is satisfied if he sees them taking unhurried, measured strides without stumbling or slipping. Where there is no track, on steep grassy slopes, on rounded boulders, on easy rock faces, on snow and ice, he can see if the fledgling mountaineer has the capacity required for the long and difficult excursions. Although mountaineering is not a specialised form of sport, but a very natural activity which most people can undertake, there are still considerable differences in a person's adaptability. Where one person will move around easily, assuredly and without fear, another becomes frightened and stiff with terror. Quite apart from physical fitness, the mental approach can also play a decisive part.

The first excursion into the mountains is decisive for the further development of the mountaineer. If the capacities are strained to the utmost or even exceeded, then disillusion can soon set in. The "hump" is no longer a thing of beauty and the over-strained body prevents the mind from appreciating the magnificence. But when the first long trip into the mountains is accomplished without strain, and demands on physical and mental resources are kept within bounds, so that the body is still fresh, leaving the mind free to take in all the impressions of nature, it is then that enthusiasm is aroused. After this first trip to the Glärnisch, my neighbour took me along with him many times. We then climbed over the heights of the Altenalp on a misty day in the autumn. This was real rock-climbing for the expert, even if it was technically easy. But the most exciting thing about it was that we were climbing with ropes. Rope-climbing for the first time on the mountain is a procedure with something mystical about it, which makes one feel the need for celebration. A link was at that moment forged between two or three people which could mean the difference between life and death. The two or three became a single unit: the roped party.

Difficult ascents are as a rule carried out by roped parties. The lone climber remains an exception even if in the last few years some very difficult solitary ascents have been accomplished, such as the north face of the Matterhorn in winter by a new route. The feats of a Walter Bonatti on the north face of the Matterhorn, or of a Michel Darbellays in the Eigerwand, call for the ultimate in endurance, experience and courage, and find few imitators. When ropes are used properly, greater security is obtained; but more than that, it gives a closer correspondence to human life. There is much satisfaction if, during a difficult climbing section, one has the feeling of being bound by the rope to a comrade. For the mountaineer there can hardly be a greater pleasure than to pay out the rope while standing against the warm rock on a narrow ledge.

After the pure rock of the sub-alpine regions, one approaches the attractions of expeditions through rock and ice. Climbing difficulties do not dominate in this case.

Rock climbing.
Where is the boy without a
natural urge to climb something
and to surmount obstacles?
(We say "boy" but it could
just as well be "girl".) Real
mastery is only achieved here
by continual effort.
The guide Eugen Steiger from
Walenstadt, one of the really
great masters of rock climbing,
negotiates a difficult section
in the limestone rock of the
Säntis massif. Rock climbing
can be quite well achieved
with a combination of theory
and practice. The outstanding
experts, however, have a
natural talent as well.

Opposite: Handholds and footholds. Climbing is developed from walking. Using only the legs for climbing is less exhausting than using the arms as well. The principal use of hands and arms is to give the body the necessary balance.

Below: East of the sixth Kreuzberg in the Säntis massif lies a rock pillar which, because of its shape, is called Daumen (the Thumb). Scaling the Daumen above the Rheintaler Egg is a short but very difficult climbing feat (Grade VI), which it is possible to ascend without pitons because the climber is able to secure himself against a jagged ridge of the adjoining fifth Kreuzberg jutting at an angle above him.

Ascending the Daumen of the sixth Kreuzberg.
High above the Rhine valley the climber swings through the air if, in the course of this extremely difficult section of a few metres, he loses his balance, or if he makes a maladroit movement. Strength and exper-

tise are required for negotiating a pitch like this.

Supreme mastery of climbing technique is here demonstrated by Franz Grubenmann from the Säntis region. This legendary climbing exponent, who helped several people through many a ticklish predicament in the mountains, met with a fatal accident on a comparatively safe overhanging section.

Legs spread wide, Franz Grubenmann levers himself up the first stage of the ascent of the Daumen. The safety rope runs at an angle up to the west ridge of the fifth Kreuzberg, where his companion is sitting behind a rock projection. This climbing expedition is difficult from the start.

The rock is uninviting, handholds and footholds are often very small. Concentrated and unhurried, Frank Grubenmann makes the ascent with all the agility of a cat. There he goes! The weight of the body is borne on the legs. Franz Grubenmann is the only climber I have known to ascend the Daumen, which he has scaled dozens of times, without securing himself in the normal way on the fifth Kreuzberg.

The front spikes of the
crampons bite into the bare ice.
The securing rope passes
through a karabiner fastened to
a firmly anchored ice-screw.

But the expeditions become more extensive, strenuous and dangerous. One often leaves the hut shortly after midnight, so that before the sun rises one has passed through the areas threatened by rock falls. Weather conditions begin to play a much greater part than in the areas of pure rock. Fresh snowfall during the night can make it impossible to continue the tour, while a sudden drop in temperature can make an otherwise dangerous trip more easy to accomplish. But always the rope is there like a miraculous nerve linking one to one's companions. The rope makes us feel stronger and more ambitious. The rope is not a nice-looking piece of equipment to decorate the rucksack, though to see some mountain climbers one might well think so. The rope is there for security, frequently used to descend. It is in the real rock-climbing regions that one learns the best securing techniques and where they are really more necessary than on many tours through the Alps where even among the guides there are sometimes the oddest securing methods. For instance, there is no security when two climbers simply move or climb one behind the other on the rope, for if one of them happens to lose his footing, it is almost certain that he will pull his companion with him into the abyss.

The usual method in rock areas is for two people to be roped together. The arrangement is, however, more flexible with three. And larger roped parties are never required for difficult and long excursions, except perhaps when two separate roped parties tie themselves together to negotiate a specially difficult section. When the leader on the rope climbs up a difficult piece of rock or ice, he is held secure by his companion. But if the companion is actually to give the necessary security, he must himself be secured. This securing of oneself while securing someone else is very important, a point to which it is worth while to give the greatest attention. Securing oneself is best achieved on firm rock projections or blocks, or with the aid of face hooks and ice jacks. The technique of securing has made great strides during the last few years. There are now far more mountaineers than there were twenty years ago who undertake the most difficult ascents. This has brought with it a greater wealth of experience of which the climber can and should avail himself. In the first four decades of this century, when ascents of the greatest difficulty were being made in the limestone eastern Alps, such as the Wilden Kaiser, the Karwendel, the Dolomites and also in the pinnacles of the Mont Blanc range, the Swiss mountains, with few exceptions, were left undisturbed. The Swiss mountaineer in general found no pleasure in the vertical walls of rocks and pillars. He chose the easy ascents, especially the ridges. This is no criticism of the Swiss mountaineer, among whom there were always quite outstanding experts, but it explains why the country of our Central Alps did not figure so large in the development of alpine techniques. Rock-climbing as a sport was for a long period frowned on by wide circles of Swiss alpinists, and the idea of a scale of difficulty was always resolutely opposed. Opinion has now changed completely. It is astonishing to record the accomplishments of Swiss mountaineers both in their own country as well as in mountains all over the world. I think of the Everest expedition, Dhaulagiri, Pumori and other high mountains as well as the difficult ascents of the Alps themselves. At the end of the 'thirties, the mountains of Switzerland were regarded as adequately surveyed in the traditional sense of alpinism, that is ascents with technical aids limited to safety equipment. But now a new generation of mountaineers has opened up a second period of discovery which started in 1945, and which has not stopped at the steepest faces. Some splendid climbing areas, such as the Churfirsten, overlooking the Walensee, were opened up for the first time ever in the post-war years.

A young person with a natural urge to travel and accomplish something, who has fallen under the spell of mountaineering, will want to develop his physical and mental forces still further in order to tackle the most difficult excursions. Only when the body is in perfect training can one fully enjoy long and difficult tours—and mountaineering should always remain an enjoyable experience and a satisfying pastime in the most beautiful of all worlds.

Mountaineering as a suicidal "battle" is either a malady or a bombastic exaggeration. It is time that an end was made to all descriptions of alpine achievements in terms of battle and victory, conquest and mastery, death faces and killer mountains. It is not only the gossip papers which resort to this jargon, it can also be found in books about mountains. It is no coincidence that such language became fashionable during the fascist era. Then the call was for heroes, and their deeds shone the more brightly against a fearsome description of the natural features of the mountains and bloodcurdling accounts of the difficulties and dangers to be faced. Mountains as subjects to be conquered and subdued? Impudent and pompous rubbish! Man should be able to rejoice at such a wonderful recreation and be grateful when in the course of his excursions, whether difficult or easy, that he can experience nature in all its beautiful and splendid glory.

The Dangers of Mountaineering

Herbert Maeder

Is mountaineering dangerous? If the question is put to someone who is not a mountaineer, then the answer will invariably be "yes". For many people mountaineering is synonymous with risking one's life, a foolish gamble, an irresponsible activity. Every news item on the radio and in the newspapers, recording another accident, is quoted to show that mountaineering and everything connected with it should be condemned and that only the gentle walk on well-trodden paths is free from danger. But the mountaineer will be more discriminating in his answer. There are many answers between the simple affirmative and the view that it is "no more dangerous than driving a car" or that "life is always full of dangers". The question is provocative. It generalises too much. But let us take it as a start.

I think back on good friends, on companions who have roamed with me in climbing parties and who are no longer alive today because the dangers were greater than themselves. When I call to mind all these fine people, well trained and well equipped, who will never again grip the sun-warmed rock, who will never again breathe the sharp cold air as they leave the hut in the depths of the night, then I believe that mountaineering is dangerous. To assert that mountaineering is not dangerous at all is the merest self-deception. Anyone who thinks that climbing mountains is without its dangers will hardly be in a position to devote his whole attention to recognising them and exercising his judgement accordingly. But it is just the timely recognition and the correct assessment of the danger which enables us to grapple with it. The clearer one is able to recognise it, the less dangerous mountaineering becomes. But ability to recognise it must be acquired by the mountaineer through studying literature on the subject and through careful observation in the mountains.

There are two kinds of danger for the mountaineer. The first kind arises from the nature of mountains themselves: rock falls, avalanches, ice-breaks, sudden changes in the weather; they are therefore described as the objective dangers. The second category arises from the mountaineer himself, the subject, and are therefore described as subjective dangers: deficient equipment, false assessment of the difficulty, excessive ambition. Careful study of the opportunities and the experience gained from several mountain excursions make it possible for the careful mountaineer to reduce the objective dangers to a minimum. The subjective dangers can, however, be almost completely eliminated. The mountaineer can never be too critical of himself. Over-estimating one's own abilities can easily lead to disaster. Accidents which cannot be attributed to some fault or other seldom occur in the mountains.

The Objective Dangers

The object is the mountain, this wonderful sculptured mass of barren land, a gift to mankind as one of the last oases of quiet, beauty and adventure. Far and wide over the green central plains rise the ice-covered peaks of the high mountains, while the mountains of pure rock display the bold and rugged beauty of their shapes at closer range. Rock, snow and ice are the materials of which the mountain is formed. They determine for the most part the shape of the peaks, and their fissures and structure are the background to the principal dangers of the Alps: falling rocks, stone falls, avalanches, ice falls and crevasses.

The Rock. Anyone passing through the mountains will be surprised at the bold shapes of the rocks. Pinnacles and needles pierce the sky and walls of rock rise upwards sheerly, and by comparison the works of man seem very insignificant. But anyone climbing through the mountains learns about rock from close at hand. Even if he knows nothing of geology, he can discern the difference between the rough, firm granite of the Bergell, the flaky brittleness of the Ringelspitz, the massive limestone rock of the Gastlosen or the Kreuzberge and the crumbling mountain limestone of the Eiger. Crumbling rock is the despair of the climber, while in the firm rock he feels himself secure and relaxed. Why not therefore leave the crumbling rock alone? Because it is just that some of the most beautiful and attractive peaks are built of crumbling rock and because short sections of crumbling rock may be found on some routes that consist mostly of firm rock. The mountaineer must therefore learn how to climb through these sections safely. Handholds and footholds can never be used for pulling oneself upwards, only for very careful application of foot pressure. The best climbing experience can be obtained in crumbling rock which is not too difficult. Anyone climbing carefully and cleanly is not only considering his own safety, he also avoids endangering the climbers below him. Stones dislodged while climbing can often be dangerous in the more frequented areas and can be the worst of all objective dangers.

It is not only those routes that are known to pass over crumbling rock which demand the greatest caution. Rock on routes known to be solid is exposed to wide ranges of temperature and rainfall, and subject to erosion as well. The climber must test every handhold and foothold before bringing any weight upon it. In the case of footholds, which after all have to bear the whole weight of the body, a sharp kick is given against the rock with the sides of the sole. Handholds are tested for strength, standing with both feet firmly planted, and with a secure grip for the other hand. Footholds and handholds can break off, but larger blocks and slabs can tip over, when loose, taking the climber with them into the abyss. It is surprising how even a very large piece of stone, weighing several tons, can be delicately balanced, resting precariously on the ground beneath. Water penetrating into the rock clefts often freezes and thaws repeatedly, exerting an immense expansive pressure.

When using artificial aids to climbing, it is still necessary to have regard to the quality and structure of the rock. There are rocks where every piton can be easily anchored and where there is no great risk of falling, while elsewhere badly faulted and crumbling rock can cause the pitons to be pulled out one after the other. Seasoned climbers call these "zip fasteners". Just as when climbing without aids, the important thing is for the stance to be absolutely secure—a firm projection, stone block or a reliable piton. Failure of foot and handholds is a factor monotonously repeated in accident reports. This objective danger can be greatly reduced by using the utmost care and observing the golden climbing rule: always be firmly secured at three points.

Stone falls threaten mountaineers mostly in grooves and clefts, as well as in rock faces where ice has penetrated and on icy faces with patches of rock between. Frozen stones work loose under the effect of the sun's rays or a general rise in temperature. They fall together into gorges and hollows and, depending upon the quantity of loose stones deposited, can often set off a whole avalanche. The continuous weathering of the rock is the reason for a never-ending supply of stones. It is regrettable that every year there are climbers who come to grief because of stone falls. The stone fall is not just a piece of bad luck to which the mountaineer is always exposed: it is a natural phenomenon which the mountaineer must learn to recognise through observation. Very soon he will be able to determine where stone falls are likely to occur and where they are not. When planning his climb he will avoid any route which is exposed to the danger; but if he must cross or climb through parts which are exposed to such danger, he will do so if possible before the sun's rays become effective. Routes exposed to the danger of stone falls, especially north faces, should not be negotiated without a protective helmet. The light and practical plastic helmet, often a subject of ridicule a few years ago in mountaineering circles, has now been accepted by the more thoughtful climbers as indispensable. Already they have saved many lives and can be recommended for use on many normal mountain excursions as well.

No stone falls occur on ridges. These natural ladders to the sky cannot be too strongly recommended as routes for ascent. Even on very steep rock faces, the climber is usually safe from falls of stone, for the stones whistle past him through the air. Especially dangerous are ascents which involve crossing clefts in the mountain sides, which seem to offer less difficulty and are therefore to be preferred to the steep ridge or the vertical face. But what is technically easier is often the more dangerous. During summer periods, when the difference between day and night temperatures is at its greatest, the danger of stone falls is increased. When, in winter, the range of temperature is least, the danger is reduced almost to nothing. Routes which are extremely dangerous in summer can be safely negotiated in mid-winter. When they made the first ascent of the north face of the Eiger at the end of December 1963, a face notorious for its dangerous stone falls, the party consisting of Paul Etter, Ueli Gantenbein and Sepp Henkel, for instance, never saw or heard any loose stones. Winter ascents of the more difficult routes, which have become more popular among young climbers during the last few years, bring not only greater exertion and difficulty, but also less danger.

Snow and ice. The man from the plains who comes for the first time in summer to the high mountain regions, to the Jungfraujoch for example, is surprised and entranced to see enormous masses of snow and ice during the hottest time of the year, perhaps only a few kilometres from a bathing beach. The mountaineer, too, never fails to react to this change of scenery and climate with excitement, astonishment and pleasure. All precipitation at a height of more than 3500 metres occurs in the form of snow. Even on the heights of the Säntis (2501 metres) only 25 per cent of the annual precipitation is, in fact, rain. In our latitudes, the height of 2500 metres is the limit of eternal snow. Even the fiercest summer heat is not strong enough to melt the Säntis snowfields. The snow which falls during summer and winter on our upper mountain regions feeds the glaciers which flow down from the high peaks and forms what amounts to a national symbol far beyond the circle of mountaineers.

Snow is of the greatest importance to the mountaineer, an element ever present in the highest regions. Snow is not merely the light feathery substance in which we lightheartedly leave our ski tracks and which rewards a climb of five hours with a descent lasting thirty minutes. Snow involves those twin dangers: avalanches and snow cornices; it is also the ice in the rocks and the deceptive bridge over the crevasse that is as deep as a cathedral spire.

What is snow, really? Crystallised water, of course. Professor Dr W. Paulcke, a leading authority on snow phenomena, in a unique catalogue of its dangers, calls snow a rock, just like ice, even though it is something very variable and transient. There is something to be said for this definition, as it helps us to understand a whole series of features of the utmost importance to the mountaineer. Snow—as rock—consists of minerals, namely ice crystals. These minerals tend to stratify as other minerals do. According to their incidence, changes take place in these snow strata. Movement and compression diminish or increase. The compactness of the snow and the contours of the country where the snow falls give some guidance as to the dangers which threaten the mountaineer from the snow.

Avalanches and snow ledges are sources of danger every year to many people in the Alps. Not only are the local inhabitants and people who work in the upper regions, particularly those engaged on constructional work for power stations, victims of fatal accidents in the snow, but skiers and mountaineers are, too. While the mountaineer who keeps to the recognised tracks can enjoy his winter recreation in full security, the climber away from these paths is continually exposed to snow hazards, and the way to avoid such dangers is to recognise them. The climber ascending on skis in winter, spring or even in summer, must not only be fully equipped, but he must know something about snow and the configuration of the land and how these react upon each other. Before starting a tour it is not enough simply to listen to reports from the snow and avalanche observation station at the Weissfluhjoch and to assume that, if

242

the report is favourable, one is free from danger. The reports from the Weissfluhjoch are extremely valuable indications only, but the climber must never forget that if there is a heavy fall of snow or a sudden rise in temperature, snow conditions can change in hours. The warnings from the station must not be disregarded; they are based on meticulous observations and upon experience. The Institute is available on request for local forecasts also.

If there is a general avalanche danger, ski excursions are suicidal. A general danger of avalanches is evident if large masses of snow fall during a high wind. Danger can continue long after the snow has fallen because of the effect of wind alone. Wind is the greatest spoilsport for the alpine skier. In a very short time, it can carry off enormous masses of snow which break off at the slightest touch as they have no substantial grip on the ground below.

Where the danger of avalanche arises, no sensible person will venture. More hazardous for the climber is the partial danger of an avalanche which is unavoidable so long as there is snow on the mountains. By studying the outline of the snow it will be clear what combination will lead to an avalanche. When judging snow conditions, the mountaineer must think first in terms of the snow outline. What causes conditions which set off an avalanche are not visible on the snow surface. Even hardened mountaineers often know surprisingly little about snow formation. Furthermore, this knowledge is the more vital as it can make all the difference between life and death. Where the whole of the annual precipitation is in the form of snow, the danger from avalanches is ever present. Midsummer avalanches in the mountains have claimed their toll of victims. Also in the summer, when there has been a period of bad weather, the danger of avalanches often increases. The snow lies on smooth rock and on firm layers of *firn* and ice, and when the temperature rises the melting snow makes the most slippery surface imaginable. One of the most serious disasters in the history of mountaineering, the fall of five guides and nine trainee guides with them on the Aiguille-Verte on July 1, 1964, was due to their slipping from a snow ledge.

Cornices. When the wind blows the snow over the crests, ridges and ledges of the high plateau, it causes something like a sheet of snow to form. "They're spooking" *(es guxt)* as the climbers say, when they see against the clear dark blue skies the dazzling white streamers of snow. Where this occurs, snow is being carried away, and on the lee sides cornices are formed, which are very picturesque to the eye but very dangerous for the mountaineer. When snow is falling in our Alps, the wind is nearly always blowing from between the south-west and north-west and the cornices mostly overhang on the east and north-east sides. Somewhat rarely, where the winds frequently change direction, cornices are formed on both sides of a ridge. Cornices are a direct danger for the climber—they are liable to collapse as soon as the foot touches them. But they also build up danger in another way: the accumulated masses of drift snow on the overhanging lee slopes create a serious danger of avalanche. Stepping on to these cornices leads to serious accidents every year. They are all the more treacherous because they are often not recognised for what they are. When the climber reaches a peak, he feels, after negotiating the steep ascent, quite safe and sound on the fine, almost level surface of the summit. There is virtually nothing to give the impression that this fine surface projects like a balcony over the abyss and that the solid-looking peak is, in reality, only a narrow ledge. This is especially the case if the ascent has been made on the side opposite to the cornice and the treacherous scintillating snow is out of sight so that it is easy to be deceived. Mist and driving snow can reduce visibility to a few metres and the danger of stepping on to a cornice is correspondingly increased, with the possibility of falling down with it, or sliding out over it. Ascents through northern and eastern flanks often lie within the range of overhanging cornices liable to break off at any time. The degree of danger from this source depends on the size of the drift and weather conditions. In the course of such ascents, cornices must often be knocked away or burrowed through, in order to reach the summit. This dangerous operation must only by carried out when the mountaineer is firmly secured.

Ice avalanches and ice breaks. Where glaciers break off above steep layers of rock and expose their glistening, blue-green ice to view, there in that world of fantastic beauty ice avalanches can occur. They thunder down when the movement of the glacier has reached its critical point, which may occur at any time, summer or winter, during the coldest night or the hottest day. Where ice avalanches threaten there is no protection, there are no tactics to adopt to escape the danger. The warmth of the sun has an effect only on the smallest ice breaks. These minor breaks are quite dangerous enough, but their danger zones may be crossed either at night or in the early morning. But the mountaineer must never assume he is safe simply because the temperature is below freezing point. He should avoid the places where the danger exists. Where they cannot be avoided, he should pass through the zone as quickly as possible and, so far as the danger from crevasses allows, not roped to his companions and at least fifty metres apart from them. Ascents such as the "corridor" of the Grand Combin, where the climber is exposed to the danger of ice falls for more than an hour, even under the best snow conditions, are avoided by the calculating mountaineer. It is just this ascent, however, which is performed as a pleasant ski excursion by many people blissfully unaware of any danger.

Glacier crevasses. The snow that falls as light as a feather changes to *firn* and compact ice which, in the form of a glacier, covers the hollows and valleys between the peaks of the high mountains. The largest and longest glaciers of today give us an idea of what Switzerland was like during the ice age. The Aletsch glacier is 26 kilometres long and an average of 250 metres deep. At the Konkordiaplatz it has a depth of ice varying between 600 and 800 metres. On an average the Aletsch glacier moves between 40 and 60 centimetres a day, 180 to 200 metres a year down the valley. The Lower Aar glacier is the second longest, with a length of 16 kilometres, followed by the Gorner and Fiescher glaciers, each 15 kilometres long.

The glaciers are to a greater or less extent cut by fissures, depending on the homogeneity of the rock bed. Large glaciers move down their valley at an average rate of forty centimetres a day. The movement is greater in the middle of the glacier, and slower at the sides. The distortion which this sets up causes marginal crevasses to occur. Transverse crevasses occur where the rock bed has a marked downward slope over a short distance; lengthwise crevasses are formed mainly at the end of the glacier, where the glacier bed becomes wider and the ice can spread itself sideways. Over steep ledges of rock, the glacier breaks up completely. A medley of ice towers, walls, crevasses and pinnacles is formed, marking the ice fall. Ice falls are mostly difficult to negotiate, as there is an ever-present danger from falling fragments. A special type of transverse crevasse is the marginal crevasse or *bergschrund*. This arises where steep *firn* and ice ledges or rock faces meet the less steep hollows of *firn*. In contrast to the immovable rock and the layers of *firn* and ice on the steep faces which scarcely move at all, here the glacier movement is set off without hindrance.

The glacier which is free of snow and compact, as it appears in midsummer and autumn in its lower sections, has little danger for the experienced mountaineer. The fine gravel on the ice makes it easier to cross and often means that crampons can be dispensed with. It is the snow-covered glacier which is dangerous. Crevasses are treacherously concealed by newly fallen snow. Experienced climbers are able to determine from the formation of the glacier those areas which are specially dangerous, but there is no absolutely reliable sign. How otherwise can one explain the fatal accident which befell so experienced a mountaineer as the Frenchman Louis Lachenal, the first man to climb a peak of 8000 metres? Lachenal was descending on his skis through the Vallée Blanche (Mont Blanc), a run which thousands have made without using ropes and which is known as a particularly fine descent from the high mountains, when a crevasse opened up under his skis as they passed over a long, seemingly harmless downward slope. A treacherous lengthwise fissure became the icy grave of a man who was more familiar with the mountains than most. Lachenal, perhaps the most famous of alpinists and guides, was not the first to have met his death on glacier snows. One of the first commandments of the Alps is this: On snow-covered glaciers always rope yourselves, three or four people together if possible. Countless mountaineers owe their lives to the strict observance of this rule. But the rule is often not applicable when the snow is being negotiated on skis. The danger of falling through is less because the weight is distributed along the whole length of the ski. There is one other smaller danger: many climbers rope themselves together when making the ascent of a glacier, but want to descend unroped. A descent with ropes assumes complete teamwork by the roped party, all of whom are experienced in ski technique under all snow conditions. A roped company which does not travel smoothly and provokes falls is possibly exposed to more danger than a party which negotiates glaciers without ropes but crosses the snow bridges as lightly as possible without putting undue pressure on them. Descending a glacier without ropes—that is a very difficult problem. Theory and practice often give conflicting advice. There are first-class mountain guides who adhere strictly to the "ropes only" rule on their instructional courses, but who do not observe this when making excursions on their own account. Many factors have to be taken into consideration: the consistency of the glacier and of the snow, the extent of the snow, the technical ability and knowledge of the Alps possessed by the members of the party, knowledge of the region, and visibility conditions. To rope or not to rope may well be a life or death matter and no mountaineer should disregard it. Needless to say, roping together here means roping properly with "Gstältli" or climbing belts, and an adequate supply of rope for the leading and last members of the party and fixed climbing loops on the rope (bowlines, climbing clips).

Cable and mountain railways which take their passengers into the glacier regions offering glacier descents to ski enthusiasts, only few of whom can have had any mountain experience, are a most serious menace. Where Louis Lachenal was unable to recognise the dangers, how will the inexperienced downhill skiing enthusiast recognise them? Danger threatens every descent on a glacier with other than harmless *firn* surfaces, even when the local organisation keeps watch on the ski descents and marks the best and safest of them with stakes.

Peaks which cannot be reached by cable and mountain railways are now accessible to glacier aircraft and helicopters. Skiing enthusiasts, without any alpine experience, are thus able to enjoy the longest and finest glacier descents. The mountaineer regards this modern development with some anxiety. Not only are areas which used to enjoy complete peace and quiet invaded by noise and activity, but there are other pitfalls for the airborne tourist. Perhaps a little stiff on leaving the aircraft cabin, as the body has not been warmed and loosened up by several hours of climbing, he then starts a long descent, often exposed to the dangers of crevasse and avalanche. Very seldom does he carry the equipment which the conventional ski-climber regards as indispensable.

Weather changes. Every year, when bad weather suddenly sets in, many mountaineers are in trouble. The weather is an ally whose moods are difficult to predict. When the weather is fine, the climber can start off on his expedition, encouraged by a favourable weather forecast, and even then find himself a few hours later exposed to a most terrible storm. There is hardly any region of the Alps where the weather is predictable; there are only degrees of uncertainty. Some of the most exposed peaks, such as Mont

Below: Mass ascent of Monte Rosa. Walking in close formation on glacier snow is a serious lack of regard for general safety rules.

Opposite: Avalanche of newly fallen snow in the north flank of the Säntis. In the high mountains the danger of avalanches is not confined to winter. Where precipitation throughout the year is in the form of snow, this danger is ever present.

Opposite, above: "Missing in the mountains!" A search party with radio transmitter in the Galenstock area.
Opposite, below: Helicopter and conventional aircraft have been used increasingly during the last few years for rescue work in inaccessible parts of the mountains. In bad weather, the use of these machines is limited, and for that reason rescue teams on foot are indispensable. Rescue work in difficult areas requires a well-trained and technically equipped "ground" team.

Blanc or the Eiger, are those most subject to sudden changes of weather. Even when the weather is generally fine in summer, local falls of snow can occur. A sudden change in the weather was the cause of ten climbers losing their lives in the Mont Blanc massif during the first week of August 1966. The morning of August 1st was bathed in sunshine, but already by the early afternoon storms and snow were howling round the highest summits of the Alps. A cold front had advanced from the north-west towards the Alps with such speed that many mountaineers found themselves without time to break off their tour and seek shelter in the nearest hut. Cold fronts like this, accompanied by a sharp drop in temperature and heavy snow storms right down to the valleys, occur every year in the Alps. Nearly always some people lose their lives. There are certain warning signs of such weather development. Observation of the cloud formation and the barometer, which the climber can carry with him in the form of an aneroid altimeter, can protect the mountaineer from being taken un-awares. Cold fronts announce themselves through distinct cloud types, especially the hooked cirrus rapidly changing their shape. The air pressure suddenly falls, often the day before the weather changes, but in some cases only two or three hours before-hand.

Just as the cold front is a menace to the mountaineer in the summer, the warm front threatens the skier in winter. Warm air from the Atlantic is pushed upwards over masses of cold air covering the central lowlands. Dry snow changes its composition in a matter of minutes, becoming damp and sticky. Up to about 3000 metres it can turn to rain even in the depths of winter. The warm fronts of winter rarely form with the rapidity of the cold fronts in summer, and the number of casualties is therefore less.

The mountaineer is continuously exposed to the weather. The weather decides if an expedition is successful or not, more dramatically it makes the difference between life and death. Ernst Hostettler, mountaineer and weather prophet, has dedicated the best part of several decades on the Säntis to a study of weather conditions. He says "The mountaineer should do this far more often: look at the sky and watch the clouds! He should be able to read the language of the heavens."

It is seldom that the victims of disasters due to the weather are found among the elite of the climbing fraternity. In the first place, the leading mountaineers have had a wide experience of judging weather; secondly, their bodily constitution is so good that they can face up to the caprices of the weather better than the average tourist; and thirdly, they are so well equipped that they have no hesitation in pitching a tent in rock or snow. With suitable tent equipment and being sound in wind and limb, mountaineers have been able to stay alive for several days of storm and cold on ex-posed rock faces. In contrast, many an ill-equipped climber on an easy route has met his death from storm and cold after one single night in his tent. On any major excur-sion into the high mountains, the wise mountaineer will take with him a roll-up tent, cooker, sufficient food and appropriate warm clothing. The rucksack may be a little

251

heavier. But it is a relief to know that one will not be exposed to facing a change in weather without protection.

The Subjective Dangers

The subject is man, the fallible lord of creation. Not at all built to withstand a long sojourn at inhospitable heights, he is now more remote than ever from his origins, through the onward march of civilisation. But this man who has learnt how to race over asphalt roads or by railway through whole countries in a single day, who ploughs through the oceans in fast ships, and who competes with the birds flying across the skies, sometimes feels the longing to get back to his original state. Back to the original means of locomotion on two legs, back to the cold nights under the stars, looking down on white peaks, back to the smell of pinewood in the warm mountain forest, back to meeting the challenge of difficulties confronting man just where the world is at its most beautiful, in the mountains. Rock, snow and ice threaten in many ways our two-legged warm-blooded man who embarks on mountaineering with scarcely any of those natural advantages which the Creator has given in such profusion to the four-legged and winged inhabitants of the Alps.

If the mountaineer succumbs to an objective danger, if, for instance, he is killed by stones falling down into a dangerous gorge, it is not a matter of chance that he has succumbed to this objective danger as such. Why did he pass through a gorge subject to such falls? Why did he pass through at a time of day when the warm rays of the sun were beating down on the rocks rising above the gorge, causing the stones to be dislodged and to tumble down? If he was unaware that he was passing through a danger zone, then it was false judgement and ignorance which were the real cause of the accident. If he did know of the danger, then he knowingly faced a considerable hazard. The real causes of the accident are in both cases of a subjective nature. One can describe the cause of the accident as objective if the stones fell at that particular place at a time when, according to the best knowledge and discernment, it could not have been expected.

The mountaineer should always seek the background and exact circumstances of accidents in the Alps. He can make no better and more useful study than this. A survey of accidents in the Swiss Alps with systematic commentaries is published every year in *Alpen*, the journal of the Swiss Alpine Club. The most important details will, however, be given to him when talking to the members of rescue and emergency teams. Accidents in the Alps are a never-ending subject of discussion among mountaineers and guides.

Danger cannot be avoided merely by ignoring it and relying blindly on one's lucky star. It is surprising how seriously top-rank mountaineers go into the smallest detail of the causes of accidents and with what detail they make their own preparations and carry out their difficult expeditions. Roads and railways have brought the mountains nearer to us, huts lying up in the mountains offer a welcome shelter in inhospitable regions. But the excursion into the mountains still remains an expedition which requires planning and preparation. There must be no question of going up the mountains as if one were starting on a stroll after dinner. The preparation of a tour, the study of reports, maps, guides, avalanche and weather reports, all contribute to work up the mountaineer's enthusiasm. The joy of anticipation is often the greatest joy. Questions arise: Will the weather hold? Will the rocks be covered with ice or not? Will crampons be required, or will the ice-axe be sufficient? Are there enough ropes, spikes, pitons, cord? Is the first-aid kit complete? Has the tent been mended? Warm underclothing, leggings, second pair of gloves? Even in the course of the preparations, a single item can be vital to ensure the success of the expedition, or it can be the cause of an accident later on.

The main question remains: Is one physically and mentally fit to reach the planned goal? Are the difficulties of the planned expedition not too much from the point of view of climbing technique? Does the length of the excursion match the standards reached during training? Although alpine technical difficulties can be a relative term, they can be recognised to a certain extent. The Scale of Difficulty now adopted internationally for free climbing (I to VI) and three degrees (1, 2 and 3) for ascents where pitons are used, gives the mountaineer the possibility of obtaining a clear idea of the difficulties which lie before him. (See the Scale on page 274.) If the adoption of the Scale of Difficulty was not accepted for many years, especially in leading circles of the SAC, this was mainly due to the not very logical comment that the difficulties in the high mountains were too dependent upon weather conditions (ice, snow, rain) and the capacity of mountaineers varied too much. The Scale of Difficulty, however, is based on the technical features of the rock formation under favourable conditions. It will be clear to anyone that Grade IV under the additional effect of ice can become Grade VI, and that the degree of difficulty can increase still further from adverse weather conditions must also be taken into account. The difference in the capacity of individual mountaineers cannot be advanced as an argument against the usefulness of a graded scale. The mountaineer will be able to recognise from his own experience and assessment how to use the Scale of Difficulty. If Grade VI means "extremely difficult", this means, of course, "extremely difficult" for the fully trained and experienced mountaineer. A climber with less training and experience will probably consider that Grade II or III is "extremely difficult". The main thing is that he will at least know that ascents coming within Grade III or higher must remain beyond his capacity. That an indication as exact as possible can be of literally vital importance will be obvious for the alpinist travelling without guides, above all when he is planning excursions in areas with which he is not familiar. He can then avoid tackling itineraries beyond his powers.

For long and difficult mountain expeditions, even the best climber must be fit. Any minor disorders, headaches, pains in the neck, stomach ache, insomnia, too, can have fatal results under the heavy demands of mountaineering. The mental state should correspond with the physical state. Depression, ill-humour or other mental despondency can be harmful on long expeditions. When a situation of sudden strain arises at a difficult section of the mountain, tempers can be aroused to double the danger.

If the climber can conscientiously give an affirmative answer to the basic question as to his fitness, then come the individual questions concerning equipment, the approach, the time for starting the ascent, the weather and conditions on the mountain. One's own experience, but also the careful reading of appropriate literature, magazines and textbooks about the Alps, will help one to determine the best course to take. In every respect the mountaineer of today has an easier time than the pioneers. The very fine and accurately reproduced maps of the *Eidgenössische Landestopographie* (Federal Survey Office) are at his disposal, giving an exact description of the alpine country to assist in planning and carrying out his expeditions. Together with a compass and altimeter it is possible for the climber to make accurate preparations for his trip and show the way to safety in a hut or under a tent, should the weather break up. The increase in mountaineering since the end of the last World War, with its many expeditions to the highest and most difficult peaks of the world, has led to a profusion in the supply of equipment. Although the clothing for the mountaineer consists, as it always did, mostly of wool, with its capacity to give warmth and to dry quickly, artificial fibres are now firmly established in any items of alpine equipment. One of the most important requirements for mountain climbing, the rope, formerly admired and appreciated as a product of twisted hemp, has long ago given way to the lighter, tougher rope made of artificial fibres which is less subject to damage from wet. Light wadded clothing and very robust boots with separate inner felt lining make even strenuous winter climbing possible, and handy gas cartridges help to make the fire in the cooker, even in a tent pitched high up on a rocky slope.

The equipment must be adequate for the route it is planned to follow. Missing items can lead to much embarrassment, just as much as missing gloves, rope, pitons or first-aid kit.

If the climber in the mountains is fit, trained, well equipped and prepared, what else can happen to him now?

Apart from the objective dangers which can never be completely eliminated, there are always subtle vagaries of the subconscious. It is not only the human body which is not built for the high mountain regions; the human mind is also exposed to strains and stresses for which it is not always prepared. Mental strains—fear, pride, questions of ambition—perhaps lead the climber to disaster more often than any immediate physical cause. For instance, it is no secret that accidents often occur at the end of a holiday which has been spoilt by bad weather. The unsatisfied mountaineer becomes impatient. He begins to think that he cannot possibly return home without having "done" at least one good summit, and works himself up into a subsconscious urge to undertake the trip even when he learns beforehand of unsatisfactory conditions.

Ambition often plays an important but a very dangerous part in the mountaineer's approach. Through it he is easily lured into risking himself on expeditions which are beyond his capabilities. It is especially the psychologically unstable person who is possibly not wholly satisfied in his business or home life, who is the more prone to the fatal consequences of false ambition. The overcoming of a difficult route can become a form of substitute satisfaction. For a short time it can give a certain satisfaction and pleasure but in the long run it can only be sustained by taking on new and ever more difficult expeditions.

Fear can be both useful and disastrous. It is not true that mountaineers are a community of men with an unbounded thirst for adventure and to whom fear is an unknown quantity. Almost every mountaineer has known fear. A person exposed to the forces of nature often experiences a kind of original fear without being actually conscious of it. Is it perhaps this inborn fear of being exposed to the elements which drives many a mountaineer into scrambling down to the safety of the lowland valley almost as soon as he has been able to reach the heights? It is not only on long climbing trips where the time has to be carefully allocated that this phenomenon occurs. Mountaineers seem to be subject to something almost like pain if they stay on the summit for any length of time. The world down below in the valley exercises a compelling urge to leave the heights. All right, we've managed to get to the top where we wanted to, now let's get home as quickly as possible! Fear in a particular situation, during sections of particular difficulty or danger, when the weather changes or an avalanche threatens, can be a life-saving warning signal as well as an additional danger. The question is: how does the individual react to his fear? If the climber is suddenly seized with fear during a difficult ascent with a roped party, his self-assurance completely collapses. His knees begin to tremble on the narrow ledge. If he does not succeed in reaching a foothold or in making one on a rock projection or with a spike, it is then that he is only too liable to fall. If his fear becomes apparent before the climbing starts, then he saves himself by simply withdrawing from the excursion. Anyone who has never experienced fear in the mountains is probably lacking in imagination. Anyone with powers of imagination and who can picture all sorts of possible dangers can easily become victim to a constrictive or even paralysing fear complex. It is in the ability to know oneself, in reacting correctly to any feeling of fear, in knowing when to withdraw, and in a determination to conquer one's fears that one of the finest educational attributes of mountaineering lies.

Bergell (Bregaglia)
Lower Engadine

On the track from the
Trubinasca cauldron to the
Sasc Furä hut.
Sub-tropical vegetation near
the glacier (Bergell).

From left to right:
Telephoto view from Soglio of the Sciora group in the Bergell. Scioretta (3046 metres), Sciora Dafora (3169 metres), Punta Pioda di Sciora (3238 metres), Ago di Sciora (3205 metres) and Sciora Dadent (3275 metres).

The mighty granite pyramids between the Val Albigna and the Val Bondesca are especially bound up with the names of two guides: Christian Klucker and Walter Risch. The first ascents of all these peaks were led by Christian Klucker with his clients between 1888 (Sciora Dadent) and 1893 (Ago di Sciora). Walter Risch, in a guideless ascent, conquered the east-north-east pillar of the Ago di Sciora on July 1, 1923, crossed the whole range with Alfred Zürcher on August 2, 1923, and led the first winter ascent of the Punta Pioda di Sciora on March 8, 1929.

The 800-metre high north side of the Piz Badile (3308 metres) in the Bergell is an ideal granite climbing objective. The mountaineer follows the continuous ridge of the pillar in a straight line from the start to the summit. It is difficult to avoid comparing it to the most beautiful limestone flank in the Alps, the Schleier flank on the Cima della Madonna in the Dolomites. The only difference is that the Badile wall is very much less steep. Its rock, however, is much more compact, the holds are smaller and less frequent. Here the climber has to rely on friction. This can be pleasant when the rock is dry, but a dangerous proposition in wet weather, since the lichen tends to make the rock very slippery. As far back as July 11, 1892, Christian Klucker made a guideless ascent to the over-hanging fissure, but the first complete ascent was made on August 4, 1923, by Alfred Zürcher with the guide Walter Risch in eleven hours of solid climbing.

Opposite, above: In the grey morning light, mountaineers leave the comfort of the Sasc Furä hut at the foot of the flank.

Opposite, below: On the way to the starting point. To the left is the Piz Cengalo (3370 metres) with the upper part of its north face; to the right, the Badile face forms a sharp dividing line between the sunny north-east face and the shaded north-west face.

Right: The guide Walter Belina secures his companion on the lower part of the face.

Right: Airy climbing on the Zürcher plateau. The plateau finishes up in an overhanging fissure, one of the most difficult points on the whole Badile flank. Nowhere, however, is the ascent more than Grade VI.

Opposite page
View above the Zürcher plateau into the plateau torrent of the north-east face. A storm with hail threatens a roped party of English climbers on the steep, smooth face.
The north-east wall was the scene of a dramatic incident in 1937. Two climbers from Como, Molteni and Valsechi, attempting the first ascent, were overtaken by the trained Cassin / Esposito / Ratti party, and hauled up by rope. The weather grew worse. The tent belonging to the Como party was swept away by a fall of stones. They had to spend the night completely unprotected, tying themselves to hooks. The next day, this extremely difficult ascent was continued. But Molteni and Valsechi perished from exhaustion.
For a long time the Badile face was considered one of the most difficult granite faces in the Alps. More recent, large-scale ascents in the Mont Blanc region have warranted this description. Climbing experts now consider it to be a fine achievement of V-plus difficulty.

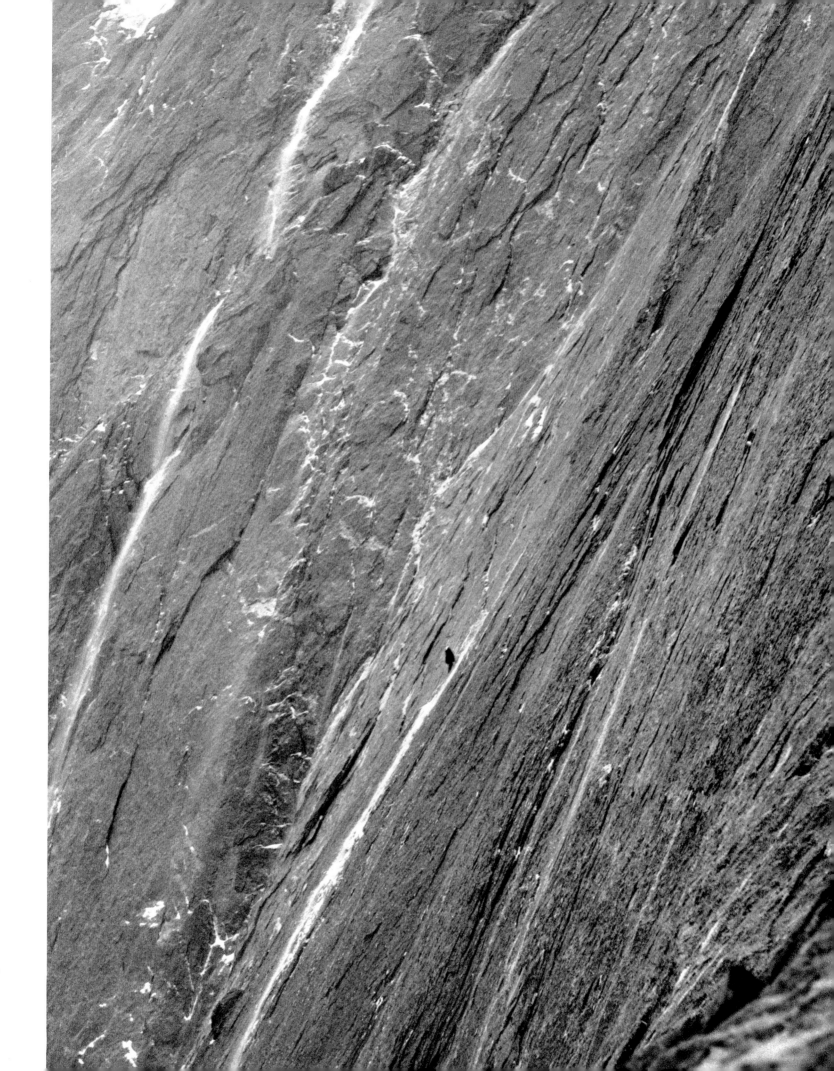

The way down from the summit of the Piz Badile (3308 metres) back to the starting point is long and tiring and this is one reason for many climbers preferring to use the flank for the descent.

Left: The normal descent leads through fairly difficult climbing sections across the Italian south flank. Over the Passo Porcellizo, the mountaineer can reach the small camping hut Natale Vaninetti, built at a height of 2600 metres by the Milan section of the Italian Alpine Club, overlooking the Val Codera.

Opposite: Above the Trubinasca Pass the mountaineer turns back into the Val Bondesca. The way down into the deep valley (Bondo lies at a height of only 823 metres) opens up the real wonders of the Bergell. From the high mountain regions with glaciers and bold rock summits one passes straight into zones of sub-tropical vegetation. The marked tracks from the Trubinasca cauldron to the Sasc Furä hut lead through a damp, steaming jungle. The descent to Bondo lies through ferns as high as a man and other plants abundant in their luxury, clearly indicating to the mountaineer that he is passing through the warm south face of the alpine barrier.

Behind the Schlosshügel of Tarasp is the start of the longest and most beautiful ridge route in the dolomite region of the Lower Engadine. Above the Piz Lavetscha (2790 metres) and the Piz Clemgia (3042 metres) a climbing tour of some ten hours leads to the Piz Pisoc (3173 metres). From the foot of the Piz Lavetscha the mountaineer can look down the Inn valley towards the mountains of Austria. On the right-hand side of the Inn valley, the Val S-charl, the Val Lischena, the Val Triazza, the Val d'Uina, the Val d'Assa and the Val Torta all open into it. The Engadine region is a very important area for the geologist. The overthrust theory is most clearly demonstrated here with the famous "windows" of the Lower Engadine.

Following double page
The Grisset, a granite offshoot
of the Bös Fulen in the Glarus
country, is picked out by the
rays of the morning sun. Its
limestone formation, with the
surrounding heights still
slumbering in the blue-grey of
the dawn, reflect an ethereal
light. Immediately above the
Grisset is the Grosse Windgälle,
further to the left are the
Scherhörner and the Clariden-
stock.

Appendices

Summary Table of Alpine Animals (Vertebrates)

Class	Group	Typical alpine species	Varieties seen in the Alps
Batrachia (amphibians)	Tailed amphibians	Alpine salamander	Alpine salamander (or mountain molch)
	Frog amphibians		Grass frog
Reptiles	Snakes	Common viper	Poisonous adder
		Aspis (or Jura) viper	Ringed adder
	Lizards	Mountain lizard	Wall lizard
Mammals	Chiroptera	Alpine bat	Little horshoe bat
			Two-coloured bat
			Nordic bat
	Insectivorous	Alpine shrew	Water shrew
			Marsh shrew
			Dwarf shrew
			Wood shrew
	Rodents	Marmot	Garden dormouse
		Vole	Field-vole
			Field-mouse
		Snow mouse	Red tree-mouse
			Mole
	Leporidae	Alpine hare	
	Beasts of prey	Mountain fox	Stone marten
		Dwarf weasel	Ermine
			Long-tailed weasel
	Artiodactyl	Chamois	Red deer
		Steinbock	
Birds	Water fowl		Common duck
	Birds of prey	Golden eagle	Kestrel
	Game birds	White grouse	
		Moorhen	
		Stone grouse	
	Swifts	Alpine swift	Black martin
	Cuckoos		Cuckoo
	Sparrows	Sand (or mountain) piper	
		Mountain swallow	Flour martin
			Rock wagtail
			Water wagtail
			Ousel
			Wren
		Alpine (rock) sparrow	Hedge sparrow
		Fallow finch	Robin redbreast
		Rock red-tit	Common redstart
		Ringed blackbird (or thrush)	
		Alpine titmouse	Hedge whitethroat
		Wall-creeper	
		Song thrush	
		Snow finch	
		Yellow finch	
		Pine greenfinch	
		Alpine (rock) crow	
		Alpine jackdaw	
		Common raven	
		Pine jay	

Scale of Difficulty for Rock Climbing

The normal Scale of Difficulty used internationally for rock climbing comprises six grades. Each grade is often subdivided into plus and minus to give a more precise indication. The scale which is always being compared and tested by the leading mountaineers in all countries, is expressed in words as follows:

Grade	Examples on limestone rock	Examples on Bedrock
I Easy	Third Kreuzberg, normal route Altmann, from the north	Pizzo Rotondo, south-east ridge Kl. Windgälle from the north or south-east
II Medium difficult	Fifth Kreuzberg, west ridge Kingspitz, normal route	Düssistock, north-west ridge Cima del Largo, normal route
III Advanced	Altmann, eastern ridge route traversing Kl. and Gr. Simelistock	Zinalrothorn, Rothorn ridge Gletschhorn, south ridge
IV Very difficult	Kl. Drusenturm, south-east ridge Hundstein, south face	Piz Badile, north side Salbitschijen, south ridge
V Exceptionally difficult	Kingspitz, north-east face Gr. Drusenturm, Burgerweg	Piz Badile, north-east face Salbitschijen Zwillingsturm, south-east face
VI Extremely difficult	Bockmattli, north face direct Drusenturm, south pillar	Grandes Jorasses Walker pillars Aiguille des Drus: Bonatti pillars

These grades give an indication of difficulties occurring in free climbing under good conditions. Within this classification, pitons serve only as securing equipment, but not as equipment for assisting movement. If, however, they are used with foot slings to assist movement, then a special scale is adopted consisting of three grades A.1, A.2 and A.3, the "A" stading for *"artificiel"*, which reveals the French origin (Mont Blanc) of this scale. Here A.1 means an easily negotiated section, A.3 a very difficult section. In describing routes as difficult, the difficulties are now generally given in detail.

Mont Rogneux, 3083 m
Mont Vélan, 3734 m
　Petit Vélan, 3201 m
　Aiguille du Vélan, 3635 m
Obergabelhorn, 4063 m
　Mittel Gabelhorn, 3685 m
　Unter Gabelhorn, 3319 m
Petit Combin, 3672 m
Petit Mont Collon, 3555 m
Pic de l'Artsinol, 2997 m
Pierre Avoi, 2472 m
Pigne d'Arolla, 3796 m
Pigne de Combavert, 2871 m
Pigne de la Lé, 3396 m
Platthorn, 3344 m
Pletschenhorn, 2737 m
Pointe Ar Pitetta, 3132 m
Pointe du Bandon, 3074 m
Pointe de Barasson, 2962 m
Pointe de Bricola, 3657 m
Pointe de Masserey, 2842 m
Pointe de Moiry, 3283 m
Pointes de Mourti
　3563 m
　3529 m
Pointe de Nava, 2769 m
Pointe d'Otemma, 3403 m
Pointe des Rayons de la Made-
　leine, 3051 m
Pointe de Tourtemagne, 3079 m
Pointe de Tsalion, 3512 m
Pointe du Tsaté, 3077 m
Pointe de Vouasson, 3489 m
Pointe de Zinal, 3791 m
Roc d'Ortsiva, 2852 m
Rosablanche, 3336 m
Rotighorn, 2958 m
Sasseneire, 3254 m
Schalihorn, 3974 m
Schölihorn, 3499 m
Schwarzhorn, 3201 m
Sex de Marinda, 2903 m
Six Blanc, 2445 m
Stellihorn
　Inner, 3409 m
　Äusser, 3405 m
Stierberg, 3506 m
Tête de Balme, 3312 m
Tête Blanche, 3724 m
Tête de Lion, 3715 m
Tête de Milon, 3691 m
Tête de Valpelline, 3802 m
Tounot, 3017 m
Tour de Boussine, 3826 m
Tournelon Blanc, 3707 m
Trifthorn, 3728 m
Tsa de l'Ano, 3367 m
Wandfluhhorn, 3589 m

Wängerhorn, 3096 m
Wasenhorn, 3343 m
Weisshorn, 4505 m
Wellenkuppe, 3903 m
Zinal-Rothorn, 4221 m

3
The Valais Alps
Theodule Pass to the Nufenen Pass

Adlerhorn, 3987 m
Albrunhorn, 2885 m
Allalinhorn, 4027 m
Almagellerhorn, 3327 m
Alphubel, 4206 m
Balfrin, 3795 m
Balmahorn, 2870 m
Bettelmatthorn, 3043 m
Bettlihorn, 2951 m
Bigerhorn
　Gross, 3625 m
　Klein, 3183 m
Blasenhorn, 2777 m
Blinnenhorn, 3373 m
Bortelhorn, 3193 m
Böshorn, 3267 m
Brudelhorn, 2790 m
Camoscellahorn, 2610 m
Castor, 4226 m
Cima d'Azoglio, 2610 m
Cima di Jazzi, 3804 m
Cima del Rosso, 2624 m
Distelhorn, 2830 m
Dom, 4545 m
Dufourspitze, 4634 m
Dürrenhorn, 4034 m
Eggerhorn, 2503 m
Egginer, 3366 m
Faderhorn, 3206 m
Faulhorn, 2677 m
Faulhorn, 2606 m
Feekopf, 3888 m
Ferichhorn, 3290 m
Fillarhorn
　Gross, 3678 m
　Klein, 3620 m
Fleschhorn, 3004 m
Fletschhorn, 3996 m
Fluchthorn, 3790 m
Furggenbaumhorn, 2985 m
Gabelhorn, 3136 m
Galenhorn, 2794 m
Galenhorn, 3124 m
Galihorn, 2577 m
Gemshorn, 3545 m

Gischihorn, 3083 m
Glishorn, 2525 m
Gobba di Rollin, 3899 m
Grabenhorn, 3371 m
Grampielhorn, 2764 m
Grieshorn, 2928 m
Gross Huwiz, 2924 m
Guggelihorn, 2351 m
Helgenhorn, 2837 m
Helsenhorn, 3272 m
Hillenhorn, 3181 m
Hohberghorn, 4219 m
Hohsandhorn, 3182 m
Holzjihorn, 2986 m
Hübschhorn, 3187 m
Jägerhorn, 3969 m
Jägihorn, 3206 m
　Jägigrat, 3350 m
Joderhorn, 3035 m
Kinhorn, 3750 m
Klein Matterhorn, 3883 m
Kummenhorn, 2754 m
Lagginhorn, 4010 m
Lammenhorn, 3189 m
Leiterspitzen, 3469 m
Lenzspitze, 4294 m
Liskamm, 4418 m
　4480 m
Ludwigshöhe, 4341 m
Merezenbachschije, 3182 m
Mittaghorn, 3093 m
Mittaghorn, 3014 m
Mittelrück, 3363 m
Monte Leone, 3553 m
Nadelhorn, 4327 m
Nollenhorn, 3185 m
Nordend, 4609 m
Nufenenstock, 2865 m
Oberrothorn, 3415 m
Ochsenhorn, 2912 m
Ofenhorn, 3172 m
Parrotspitze, 4436 m
Pizzo Cervandone, 3210 m
Pizzo Straciugo, 2712 m
Platthorn, 3246 m
Pollux, 4091 m
Portjengrat, 3653 m
Portjenhorn, 3566 m
Punta Valgrande, 2856 m
Rappenhorn, 3176 m
Riffelhorn, 2927 m
Rimpfischhorn, 4198 m
Ritzberge, 2862 m
Ritzhörner, 3047 m
Rothorn, 3287 m
Rothorn, 2887 m
Sattelspitz, 3164 m
Schijenhorn, 2890 m

Schinhörner, 2938 m
Schwarzhorn, 3108 m
Seehorn, 2437 m
Signalkuppe, 4556 m
Simelihorn, 3245 m
Sonnighorn, 3487 m
Spitzhörnli, 2726 m
Sprechhorn, 3189 m
Stecknadelhorn, 4242 m
Steinkalkhorn, 3478 m
Stellihorn, 3436 m
Stockhorn, 3582 m
Strahlhorn, 4190 m
Tällihorn, 3448 m
Täschhorn, 4490 m
Tochenhorn, 2648 m
Tossenhorn, 3225 m
Trifthorn, 3395 m
Turbhorn, 3247 m
Ulrichshorn, 3925 m
Vorder Helsen, 3105 m
Wamischhörner, 2922 m
Wänghorn, 2587 m
Wannenhorn, 2866 m
Wasenhorn, 3246 m
Weissmies, 4023 m
Zermatter Breithorn
　Westgipfel, 4165 m
　Mittelgipfel, 4160 m
　Ostgipfel, 4141 m
　Schwarzfluh, 4075 m
Zumsteinspitze, 4563 m

4
The Vaud Alps
Between the Rhone and Sanetsch

Arnenhorn, 2210 m
Cape au Moine, 2351 m
Chaux Ronde, 2027 m
Châtillon, 2477 m
Culan, 2788 m
Dent de Chamosentse, 2712 m
Dent de Corjon, 1966 m
Dent Favre, 2916 m
Dent de Jaman, 1875 m
Dents de Morcles
　Grand, 2969 m
　Petit, 2931 m
Grand Chavalard, 2898 m
Grand Muveran, 3051 m
　Petit Muveran, 2810 m
Gros Van, 2188 m
Gstellihorn, 2817 m
Gummfluh, 2457 m

Haut de Cry, 2969 m
L'Argentine, 2421 m
Le Biolet, 2292 m
Le Chamossaire, 2112 m
Les Diablerets, 3209 m
La Douve, 2170 m
La Fava, 2612 m
La Rionde, 1980 m
Le Rubli, 2284 m
Le Tarent, 2377 m
La Tournette, 2541 m
Mittaghorn, 2312 m
Mont à Cavouère, 2594 m
Mont Gond, 2709 m
Mont d'Or, 2175 m
Mont à Perron, 2667 m
Oldenhorn, 3122 m
Pic Chaussy, 2351 m
Pierre qu'Abotse, 2734 m
Planachaux, 1924 m
Pointe d'Aufalle, 2727 m
Pointe d'Avereyre, 2026 m
Pointes de Châtillon, 2368 m
Pointe des Martinets, 2637 m
Pointe de Perris Blancs, 2575 m
Rocher du Midi, 2096 m
Rochers de Naye, 2041 m
Rocher Plat, 2255 m
Rocher à Pointes, 2239 m
Sanetschhorn, 2923 m
Schlauchhorn, 2578 m
Sex Percé, 2509 m
Sex Rouge, 2845 m
Six Tremble, 2701 m
Tête de Bellalué, 2602 m
Tête d'Enfer, 2762 m
Tête à Grosjean, 2606 m
Tête Noir, 2876 m
Tête Pegnat, 2587 m
Tête à Pierre Grept, 2903 m
Tête Ronde, 3035 m
Tête Tsernou, 2709 m
Tour d'Aï, 2330 m
Tour de Famelon, 2137 m
Tour de Mayen, 2326 m
Tour St-Martin, 2901 m
Witenberghorn, 2350 m

5
The Bernese Alps
From the Sanetsch to the Lötschen Pass
and south of the Rhone

Albristhorn, 2761 m
Almengrat, First 2549 m

Alplighorn, 2329 m
Altels, 3629 m
Ammertenhorn, 2666 m
Arpelistock, 3035 m
Balmhorn, 3709 m
Bella Lui, 2548 m
Bonderspitz, 2546 m
Bürglen, 2165 m
Chamossaire, 2616 m
Daubenhorn, 2941 m
Dreimännler, 2436 m
Drunengalm, 2408 m
Elsighorn, 2341 m
Faldum Rothorn, 2832 m
Felsenhorn, 2782 m
Ferdenrothorn, 3180 m
Fitzer, 2458 m
Fromberghorn, 2394 m
Gandhorn, 2112 m
Gantrisch, 2175 m
Gehrihorn, 2130 m
Geltenhorn, 3071 m
Giferhorn, 2541 m
Gletscherhorn, 2943 m
Gross Lohner
   Vorder Lohner, 3048 m
   Mittler Lohner, 3003 m
   Hinter Lohner, 2930 m
   Klein Lohner, 2583 m
   Mittaghorn, 2677 m
   Nünihorn, 2716 m
Gross Strubel, 3243 m
Gsür, 2708 m
Hahnenschritthorn, 2833 m
Hundsrügg, 2046 m
Keibihorn, 2459 m
Kindbettihorn, 2692 m
Kirgelischeibe, 2287 m
Ladholzhorn, 2487 m
Lämmernhorn, 2804 m
La Motte, 2828 m
Lauchernspitzen, 2843 m
Lauenenhorn, 2477 m
Laufbodenhorn, 2701 m
Les Faverges, 2968 m
Mähre, 2087 m
Majinghorn, 3053 m
Männlifluh, 2652 m
Mittaghorn, 2685 m
Mont Bonvin, 2965 m
Mont Pucel, 3176 m
Niederhorn, 2077 m
Niesen, 2362 m
Niesenhorn, 2776 m
Niwen, 2769 m
Ochsen, 2138 m
Pointe d'Héremence, 2731 m
Prabé, 2042 m

Pra Roua, 2486 m
Rauflihorn, 2322 m
Regenbolshorn, 2192 m
Restirothorn, 2969 m
Riedbündihorn, 2454 m
Rinderhorn, 3454 m
   Kleines Rinderhorn, 2975 m
Rohrbachstein, 2950 m
Roter Totz, 2840 m
Rotstock, 2624 m
Schafhorn, 2697 m
Scheibe, 2150 m
Schneehorn, 3177 m
Schneidehorn, 2937 m
Seewlenhorn, 2529 m
Sex Noir, 2711 m
Sex Rouge, 2891 m
Sillern, 1977 m
Six des Eaux Froides, 2905 m
Spillgerten
   Vorder, 2252 m
   Hinder, 2476 m
Spitzhorn, 2806 m
Standhorn, 2338 m
Steghorn, 3174 m
Steinschlaghorn, 2321 m
Stockhorn, 2190 m
Tatlishorn
   Ober, 2931 m
   Unter, 2497 m
Tierhörnli, 2894 m
Torrenthorn, 2997 m
Tothorn ou Sex Mort, 2933 m
Trubelnstock, 2997 m
Tschingellochtighorn, 2735 m
Tschipparellenhorn, 2397 m
Tubang, 2836 m
Türmlihorn, 2491 m
Turnen, 2079 m
Wasserngrat, 2191 m
Wetzsteinhorn, 2781 m
Widdergalm, 2174 m
Widdersgrind, 2103 m
Wildhorn, 3247 m
Wildstrubel, 3243 m
Winterhorn, 2608 m
Zayetahorn, 2778 m

6
Bernese Alps
Lötschen Pass to the Grimsel and
Lake Thun to the Rhone

Aerlengrätli, 3193 m
Aerlenhorn, 2453 m

Aermighorn, 2742 m
Agassizhorn, 3953 m
Aletschhorn, 4195 m
   Klein Aletschhorn, 3745 m
Alpjahorn, 3143 m
Alplistock, 2877 m
Anengrat, 3716 m
Ankenbälli, 3605 m
Ankenbälli, 3164 m
Augstkummenhorn, 2880 m
Axalphorn, 2321 m
Bächlistock, 3247 m
Beichgrat, 3292 m
Berglistock, 3655 m
Bettlerhorn, 2535 m
Bettmerhorn, 2867 m
Bietenhorn, 2756 m
Bietschhorn, 3934 m
Birghorn, 3242 m
Birre, 2502 m
Blumhorn, 2499 m
Blümlisalp, 3664 m
Blümlisalp Rothorn, 3297 m
Blümlisalpstock, 3221 m
Brandlammhörner, 3108 m
   3088 m
Breitlauihorn, 3655 m
Brunberg, 2982 m
Bundstock, 2758 m
Burstspitzen, 3195 m
Büttlassen, 3192 m
Diamantstock
   Kleiner, 2839 m
   Grosser, 3162 m
Distlighorn, 3717 m
Doldenhorn
   Klein, 3475 m
   Gross, 3643 m
Dossenhorn, 3142 m
Dreieckhorn, 3810 m
   Klein Dreieckhorn 3641 m
Dreispitz, 2520 m
Dündenhorn, 2861 m
Ebnefluh, 3960 m
Eggishorn, 2926 m
Eiger, 3970 m
Ellstabhorn, 2830 m
Elwerrück, 3380 m
Elwertätsch, 3208 m
Escherhorn, 3100 m
Ewigschneehorn, 3329 m
Faulberg, 3242 m
Faulhorn, 2680 m
Fiescher Gabelhorn, 3875 m
Fiescherhorn
   Gross, 4048 m
   Hinter, 4025 m
Finsteraarhorn, 4273 m

Finsteraar Rothorn, 3530 m
Fisistock
   Innerer, 2787 m
   Äusserer, 2945 m
Foggenhorn, 2569 m
Fründenhorn, 3368 m
Fusshörner, I–XIII, 3627 m
Gallauistöcke, 2869 m
Galmihorn
   Vorderes, 3518 m
   Hinteres, 3490 m
Geisshorn, 3740 m
Gerstenhorn, 2926 m
Gletscherhorn, 3983 m
Golegghorn, 3063 m
Gredetschhörnli, 3646 m
Grisighorn, 3176 m
Grosses Fusshorn, 3626 m
Grosshorn, 3762 m
Grosshorn, 2995 m
Grubhorn, 3192 m
Grünegghorn, 3863 m
Grunerhorn, 3439 m
Grünhorn
   Klein, 3913 m
   Gross, 4043 m
Gspaltenhorn, 3437 m
Gummihorn, 2101 m
Gwächtenhorn, 3157 m
Hangendgletscherhorn, 3291 m
Hockenhorn, 3293 m
Hofathorn, 2844 m
Hohe Gwächte, 3086 m
Hohgleifen, 3278 m
   Adlerspitzen
Hohstock, 3226 m
Hörnli, 2926 m
Hühnerstock, 3307 m
Hühnertälihorn, 3179 m
Hundshorn, 2928 m
Jägihorn, 3406 m
Jägihorn, 3071 m
Juchlistock, 2590 m
Jungfrau, 4158 m
Kamm, 3866 m
Kilchfluh, 2833 m
Kistenhorn, 2785 m
Kleine Lauteraarhörner
   3737 m
   3648 m
Klein Nesthorn, 3336 m
Kranzberg, 3737 m
Krindelspitzen, 3017 m
Krutighorn, 3020 m
Läghorn, 2878 m
Lauberhorn, 2472 m
Laucherhorn, 2230 m
Lauteraarhorn, 4042 m

Lauteraar Rothörner, 3477 m
   3466 m
Lauterbrunner Breithorn, 3782 m
Lauterbrunner Wetter-
   horn, 3241 m
Lobhörner, 2566 m
   Orgelpfeife
   Daumen
   Dritter Turm
   Zipfelmütze
   Fünfter Turm
Löffelhorn, 3095 m
Lonzahörner
   3560 m
   3547 m
   3520 m
Lötschentaler Breithorn, 3784 m
Männlichen, 2342 m
Mettenberg, 3104 m
Mittaghorn, 3897 m
Mittelhorn, 3704 m
Mönch, 4099 m
Morgenberghorn, 2248 m
Morgenhorn, 3612 m
Mutthorn, 3043 m
Nässihorn, 3494 m
Nesthorn, 3824 m
Oberaarhorn, 3638 m
Oberaar Rothorn, 3463 m
Ochs, 3900 m
Olmenhorn, 3314 m
Oltschiburg, 2234 m
Oeschinenhorn, 3486 m
Petersgrat, 3207 m
Pfaffenstöckli, 3114 m
Renfenhorn, 3259 m
Ritzlihorn, 3263 m
Rosenhorn, 3689 m
Rosshörner, 3129 m
Rotstock, 3701 m
Rottalhorn, 3969 m
Sackhorn, 3212 m
Sägezahn, 2712 m
Salzhorn, 2570 m
Sattelhorn, 3741 m
Schaflägerstöcke, 2855 m
Scheuchzerhorn, 3467 m
Schilthorn, 3122 m
Schilthorn, 2970 m
Schinhorn, 3796 m
Schneehorn, 3408 m
Schönbühlhorn, 3853 m
Schreckhorn
   Grosses, 4078 m
   Kleines, 3494 m
Schwalmern, 2777 m
Schwarzhorn, 3126 m
Schwarzhorn, 2928 m

Schwarzhorn, 2658 m
Schwarz Mönch, 2648 m
Sidelhorn, 2764 m
Silberhorn, 3695 m
Setzenhorn, 3062 m
Sparrhorn, 3020 m
Sulegg, 2413 m
Stampfhorn, 2552 m
Steinlauenenhorn, 3162 m
Stockhorn, 3211 m
Strahlegghörner, 3462 m
Strahlhorn, 3200 m
Strahlhorn, 3195 m
Strahlhorn, 3026 m
Studerhorn, 3638 m
Tällerngrat, 2886 m
Tellispitzen, 3082 m
Tennbachhorn, 3012 m
Tierberg
   Hinterer, 3205 m
   Vorderer, 3111 m
Tieregghorn, 3072 m
Trifthörner, 3229 m
   3240 m
Trugberg, 3932 m
Tschingelhorn, 3577 m
Tschuggen, 2520 m
Unterbächhorn, 3554 m
Wachtlammstock, 2399 m
Walcherhorn, 3695 m
Wannehorn, 3120 m
Wannenhorn
   Gross, 3905 m
   Klein, 3706 m
Wasenhorn, 3446 m
Weisse Frau, 3652 m
Weisshorn, 3542 m
Wellhorn, 3191 m
   Kleines Wellhorn, 2701 m
Wetterhorn, 3701 m
Wetterlatte, 2008 m
Wild Andrist, 2848 m
Wilde Frau, 3259 m
Wildgerst, 2891 m
Wilerhorn, 3307 m
Wiwannihorn, 3000 m
Zahlershorn, 2743 m
Zahm Andrist, 2681 m
Zenbächenhorn, 3287 m
Zinggenstock
   Hinterer, 3041 m
   Vorderer, 2920 m

7
The Engelhörner

Aebnisgrat, 2735 m
Engelburg, 2302 m
Froschkopf, 2674 m
Gemsenspitze, 2617 m
Gertrudspitze, 2632 m
Gross Engelhorn, 2781 m
Gstellihorn
   Gross, 2854 m
   Klein, 2658 m
   Gstelliburg, 2701 m
Haubenstock, 2682 m
Hohjägiburg, 2639 m
Kastor, 2522 m
Kingspitz, 2621 m
Klein Engelhorn, 2634 m
Mittelspitze, 2634 m
Niklausspitze, 2671 m
Pollux, 2488 m
Prinz
   Oberer, 2621 m
   Unterer, 2581 m
Rosenlauistock, 2197 m
Sagizähne, 2716 m
Sattelspitzen, 2336 m
Simelistock
   Gross, 2482 m
   Klein, 2383 m
Tannenspitze, 2255 m
Tennhorn, 2520 m
Ulrichspitze, 2636 m
Urbachengelhorn, 2768 m
Vorderspitze, 2618 m

8
The Fribourg Alps

Bifé, 1561 m
Cape au Moine, 1941 m
Combifluh, 2004 m
Corbex, 1898 m
Dent de Bimis, 2157 m
Dent du Bourgo, 1908 m
Dent de Bourgoz, 1912 m
Dent de Brenleire, 2353 m
Dent de Broc, 1832 m
Dent du Chamois, 1830 m
Dent de Folliéran, 2339 m
Dent de Lys, 2014 m
Dent de Vounetz, 1816 m
Fochsenfluh, 1978 m
Folliu Borna, 1849 m

Gastlosen
  Gratfluh, 1949 m
  Vordere Spitze, 1960 m
  Aiguille de la Poire, 1965 m
  Chemigupf, 1972 m
  Grande Aiguille, 1950 m
  Glattewand, 1998 m
  Pointe Staub, 1890 m
  Gastlosenspitze, 1998 m
  Turm, 1960 m
  Grand Grenadier, 1915 m
  Marchzahn I–V, 1995 m
  Petit Grenadier, 1950 m
  Aiguille Penchée, 1935 m
  Pyramide, 1975 m
  Chat, 1944 m
  Daumen, 1940 m
  Petit Pouce, 1907 m
  Eggturm, 1936 m
  Gabeldaumen, 1854 m
  Waldeckspitze, 1919 m
  Roche Percée, 1969 m
  Öfenspitzen, 2014 m
  Pfadfluh, 2070 m
  Sparrengrat, 2096 m
  Weissfahnespitze, 2097 m
  Dünnefluh, 2091 m
  Rothespitze, 2083 m
  Hangfluh, 2076 m
  Tour de Berne, 1930 m
  Gross Turm, 2129 m
  Lochgrat, 2118 m
  Rüdigenspitze, 2130 m
  Birrenfluh, 2075 m
  Wandfluh, 2132 m
  Pointe de Rachevi, 2090 m
  Amelier, 2132 m
  Capucin, 2158 m
  Dent de Ruth, 2236 m
  Dent de Savigny, 2252 m
  Vanil de la Gobettaz, 2112 m
  Pointe à l'Echelle, 2090 m
  Jumelle, 2083 m
  Corne Aubert, 2039 m
Gros Brun, 2107 m
Hochmatt, 2151 m
Kaiseregg, 2188 m
Körblifluh, 2106 m
La Berra, 1722 m
Laubspitz, 1799 m
Les Courcys, 1864 m
Le Gros Vanil Carré, 2195 m
Le Moléson, 2002 m
Les Sex
  Petit Sex, 1886 m
  Grand Sex, 1908 m
Neuschelsflühe, 1972 m
Petit Brun, 2088 m

Pointe de Bremingard, 1925 m
Pointe de Cray, 2070 m
Schafarnisch, 2110 m
Schafberg, 2238 m
Schwarze Fluh, 2159 m
Schweinsberg, 1648 m
Spitzfluh, 1952 m
Teysachaux, 1909 m
Tzermont, 2134 m
Vanil des Artses, 1993 m
Vanil Blanc, 1826 m
Vanil du Croset, 2110 m
Vanil de l'Ecrit, 2375 m
Vanil du Gros Perré, 2208 m
Vanil Noir, 2388 m
Vanil d'Osseyres, 2015 m
Vanil de Paray, 2373 m

9
The Uri Alps
From the Grimsel up to the
Sandpass (Planura)

Alpgnoferstock, 2767 m
Bächenstock, 3008 m
Bächenstock, 2944 m
Badus [Six Madun], 2927 m
Bälmeten, 2414 m
Bärenzähn, 2857 m
Benzlauistock, 2530 m
Bergseeschijen, 2815 m
Blauberg, 3039 m
Blauhörnli, 2404 m
Brichplanggenstock, 3011 m
Bristen, 3072 m
Büelenhorn
  Gross, 3206 m
  Klein, 2940 m
Calmut, 2311 m
Chastelhorn, 2973 m
Chüeplanggenstock, 3207 m
Crispalt, 3076 m
Culmatsch, 2897 m
Dammastock, 3629 m
Dammazwillinge, 3275 m
Diechterhorn, 3389 m
Diederberg, 2658 m
Düssistock, 3256 m
Eggstock, 3554 m
Fedenstock, 2985 m
Federälpler [Wissen], 2969 m
Feldschijen, 3021 m
Fibbia, 2737 m
Fleckistock, 3416 m
Fruttstock, 2838 m

Fünffingerstöck, 2994 m
  Flamme, 2993 m
Fünffingerstock, 2926 m
Furkahorn
  Kleines, 3026 m
  Grosses, 3169 m
Galenstock, 3583 m
Gelmerhorn
  Kleines, 2605 m
  Grosses, 2630 m
  Gelmerspitzen, I–VII
  Hintere Gelmerhörner
Gemsstock, 2961 m
Gerstenhörner
  3166 m
  3184 m
  3172 m
Giglistock, 2900 m
Gletschhorn, 3305 m
Grassen, 2946 m
Griessenhorn
  Klein, 2851 m
  Gross, 3202 m
Griesstock
  Vorderer, 2662 m
  Mittlerer, 2730 m
  Hinterer, 2734 m
Grosser Schijen, 2784 m
Gurschenstock, 2865 m
Gwächtenhorn, 3375 m
Gwächtenhorn, 3214 m
Gwasmet, 2874 m
Gwasmet, 2841 m
Heimstock, 3102 m
Höch Fulen, 2506 m
Hoch Horefellistock, 3176 m
Hoch Sewen, 2965 m
Höhlenstock, 2903 m
Hüenerstock, 2889 m
Kalkschijen
  Hintere, 2880 m
  Mittlere, 2780 m
  Vordere, 2740 m
Kilchlistock, 3114 m
Krönten, 3107 m
Krüzlistock, 2717 m
Leckihorn, 3065 m
Lochberg, 3074 m
Mähren, 2970 m
Mährenhorn, 2922 m
Mäntliser, 2876 m
Mässplanggenstock, 2561
Meiggelenstock, 2416 m
Mettenberg, 2734 m
Miesplanggenstock, 2874 m
Mittagstock, 2951 m
Monte Prosa, 2736 m
Müeterlishorn, 3058 m

Muttenhorn
  Gross, 3099 m
  Klein, 3024 m
  Stotzig, 3061 m
Oberalpstock, 3327 m
  Klein Oberälpler, 3085 m
Ofenhorn, 2933 m
Pazola Stock, 2739 m
Péz Acletta, 2911 m
Péz Alpetta, 2764 m
Péz Ault
Péz Brit, 2801 m
Péz Cambrialas, 3208 m
Péz Carardiras, 2964 m
Péz Cazarauls, 3063 m
Péz Gendusas, 2980 m
Péz Giuv, 3096 m
  Giuvstöckli, I–VI
Péz Lumpegna, 2819 m
Péz Nair, 3059 m
Péz Run, 2914 m
Péz Tiarms, 2918 m
Péz Val Pintga, 2957 m
Pézza de Strem
  2876 m
  2838 m
  2810 m
  2777 m
  2649 m
Piz Alv, 2769 m
Piz Lucendro, 2963 m
Piz Orsirora, 2603 m
Pizzo Centrale, 3001 m
Pizzo di Pesciora, 3122 m
Pizzo Prevat, 2876 m
Pizzi Rotondo, 3192 m
Pizzo della Valletta, 2718 m
Poncione di Rovino, 2964 m
Pucher, 2933 m
Radlefshorn, 2591 m
Reissend Nollen, 3003 m
Rhonestock, 3595 m
Rienzenstock, 2957 m
Rinderstock, 2462 m
Rohrspitzli, 3220 m
Rossbodenstock, 2835 m
Rot Wichel, 3084 m
Ruchen
  Gross, 3138 m
  Klein, 2944 m
  Ruchen Nadel, 3024 m
Ruchen, 2628 m
Ruchen, 2812 m
Ruchenfensterstock, 2930 m
Ruchenfensterturm, 2918 m
Salbitschijen, 2981 m
  Salbittürme, I–V
  Zwillingsturm

Sasshörner
   3036 m
   2990 m
   3029 m
Sassstock, 2773 m
Schafschijen, 2840 m
Schaubhorn, 2683 m
Scherhorn
   Gross, 3294 m
   Klein, 3234 m
Schijenstock, 2885 m
Schlossberg, 3132 m
Schneehüenerstock, 2773 m
Schneestock, 3608 m
Schwarz Grat, 2017 m
Sewenstock, 2820 m
Sittliser, 2445 m
Spannort
   Gross, 3198 m
   Klein, 3140 m
   Adlerspitze
   Falkenturm
Spitzberg, 2934 m
Stäfelstock, 2918 m
Steinhaushorn, 3120 m
Stotzig Grat, 2989 m
Straligen Stöckli, 2928 m
Stucklistock, 3308 m
Sunnig Stöcke, 2110–2713 m
Sunnig Wichel, 2911 m
Sustenhorn, 3504 m
   Klein Sustenhorn, 3315 m
Sustenspitz, 2930 m
Taghorn, 2090 m
Tälistock, 3185 m
Tellistock, 2579 m
Tiefenstock, 3515 m
Tieralplistock, 3382 m
Tierberg
   Vorder, 3094 m
   Hinter, 3443 m
Titlis, 3239 m
Trotzigplanggstock, 2954 m
Tschingelstöcke, 2872 m
Uratstock, 2911 m
Wängihorn, 2148 m
Wasenhorn, 2926 m
Wendenhorn, 3023 m
Wendenstöcke, 3042 m
Wichelhorn, 2767 m
Wichelplanggstock, 2974 m
Wichelschijen, I–IV,
   2790–2840 m
Windgälle
   Grosse, 3187 m
   Kleine, 2986 m
Winterberg, 3167 m
Winterhorn, 2660 m

Winterstock
   3203 m
   3176 m
   3172 m
Wiss Nollen, 3398 m
Witenalpstock, 3016 m
Witenwasserenstock, 3082 m
Zwächten, 2995 m

10
The Ticino Alps

Basòdino, 3272 m
Bedriolhorn, 2921 m
Camoghè, 2228 m
Camoghei, 2356 m
Campo Tencia, 3071 m
Chüebodenhorn, 3069 m
Cima Bianca, 2612 m
Cima di Biasagno, 2417 m
Cima di Biasca, 2574 m
Cima di Bresciana, 2393 m
Cima di Broglio, 2394 m
Cima di Bri, 2520 m
Cima di Cardedo, 2221 m
Cima d'Efra, 2577 m
Cima di Fornei, 3056 m
Cima di Gagnone, 2518 m
Cima di Gana Bianca, 2842 m
Cima di Gana Rossa, 2786 m
Cima di Lago, 2832 m
Cima di Negroso, 2182 m
Cima di Nimi, 2190 m
Cima di Piancabella, 2670 m
Cima di Precastello, 2359 m
Cima di Rierna, 2460 m
Cima di Sassalto, 2427 m
Cima di Sgiu, 2363 m
Cima dell'Uomo, 2390 m
Colma di Pinaderio, 2461 m
Corno di Gesero, 2227 m
Corona di Redorta, 2804 m
Cristallina, 2911 m
Culpiana, 2416 m
Denti della Vecchia
   Sasso Grande, 1491 m
Gaggio, 2267 m
Grieshorn, 2928 m
Helgenhorn, 2837 m
Kastelhorn, 3128 m
La Marcia, 2381 m
Madone, 2756 m
Madone, 2395 m
Madone, 2039 m
Madone di Càmedo, 2445 m

Madone di Formazzolo, 2510 m
Madone di Giove, 2264 m
Madone Grosso, 2742 m
Marchhorn, 2962 m
Martschenspitz, 2688 m
Mognoi, 2650 m
Monte Bar, 1816 m
Monte Generoso, 1701 m
Monte Gradiccioli, 1935 m
Monte Lema, 1619 m
Monte Tamaro, 1961 m
Monte Zucchero, 2735 m
Pecianet, 2764 m
Pilone, 2191 m
Pizzo Alzasca, 2262 m
Pizzo Barone, 2864 m
Pizzo Bombogno, 2331 m
Pizzo Cadreghe, 2510 m
Pizzo di Campioni, 2769 m
Pizzo di Campello, 2660 m
Pizzo Campolungo, 2713 m
Pizzo Cassimoi, 3129 m
Pizzo Cassinello, 3104 m
Pizzo Castello, 2808 m
Pizzo dei Cavagnoli, 2836 m
Pizzo Cavegna, 2280 m
Pizzo Cavergno, 3223 m
Pizzo di Claro, 2720 m
Pizzo Cocco, 2339 m
Pizzo di Corbella, 2065 m
Pizzo del Corno, 2500 m
Pizzo Corombe, 2545 m
Pizzo Costiscio, 2244 m
Pizzo Cramalina, 2322 m
Pizzo Cramosino, 2717 m
Pizzo d'Era, 2619 m
Pizzo Fiorina, 2925 m
Pizzo Foioi, 2628 m
Pizzo Folcra, 2662 m
Pizzo Forno, 2907 m
Pizzo Galarescio, 2728 m
Pizzo Gallina, 3060 m
Pizzo Gana, 2953 m
Pizzo Grandinagia, 2774 m
Piz Jut, 3020 m
Pizzo Lago Gelato, 2617 m
Pizzo del Lago Scuro, 2647 m
Pizzo Magno, 2328 m
Pizzo Malora, 2639 m
Pizzo Masnee, 2205 m
Pizzo Massari, 2759 m
Pizzo Medaro, 2550 m
Pizzo Medola, 2958 m
Pizzo di Mezzodi, 2707 m
Pizzo Molare, 2585 m
Pizzo di Naret, 2584 m
Pizzo Nero, 2904 m
Pizzo Ogliè, 2604 m

Pizzo Orgnana, 2218 m
Pizzo Orsalietta, 2476 m
Pizzo Piancascia, 2359 m
Pizzo delle Pecore, 2381 m
Pizzo Peloso, 2063 m
Pizzo Porcarescio, 2466 m
Pizzo del Prévat, 2558 m
Pizzo Pulpito, 2616 m
Pizzo di Rodi, 2698 m
Pizzo di Ruscada, 2492 m
Pizzo di Ruscada, 2004 m
Pizzo di San Giacomo, 2924 m
Pizzo Sole, 2773 m
Pizzo di Sologna, 2696 m
Pizzo Sorda, 2884 m
Pizzo Tanedo, 2666 m
Piz dell'Uomo, 2662 m
Pizzo di Vogorno, 2442 m
Pizzo Zucchero, 1899 m
Plattenberg, 3042 m
Poncione d'Arbione, 2409 m
Poncione di Braga, 2864 m
Poncione Cavagnolo, 2764 m
Poncione dei Laghetti, 2616 m
Poncione dei Laghetti, 2445 m
Poncione di Manio, 2924 m
Poncione di Mezzodi, 2638 m
Poncione Piota, 2498 m
Poncione Pro do Rodùc, 2507 m
Poncione Rosso, 2505 m
Poncione Sambuco, 2581 m
Poncione Tremorgio, 2669 m
Poncione di Vallegia, 2873 m
Poncione di Vespero, 2717 m
Porta del Corvo, 3015 m
Ritzberg, 2591 m
Rotenkasten, 2218 m
Rosso di Ribbia, 2542 m
Sasso Bello, 2282 m
Schenadùci, 2746 m
Simano, 2579 m
Sonnenberg, 2748 m
Sonnenhorn, 2792 m
Sosto, 2220 m
Tamierhorn, 3067 m
Torrone di Nava, 2832 m
Wandfluhhorn, 2864 m

11

12

Schibe
  Hintere, 3084 m
  Vordere, 2987 m
Schiberg, 2043 m
Schijen, 2608 m
Schilt, 2299 m
Selbsanft
  Vorder, 2750 m
  Mittler, 2949 m
  Hinter, 3029 m
Silberen, 2314 m
Speichstock, 2968 m
Spitzalpelistock
  Hinterer, 2937 m
  Vorderer, 2929 m
Stoc Grond, 3422 m
Tierberg, 1989 m
Tödi
  Piz Russein, 3620 m
  Glarner Tödi, 3582 m
  Sandgipfel, 3390 m
Tschinglenhörner
  2846 m
  2849 m
Tüfelsstöck
  2960 m
  2968 m
  2919 m
Vorab
  Glarner Vorab, 3018 m
  Bündner Vorab, 3028 m
  Vorab Pitschen, 2898 m
Vorder Glärnisch, 2328 m
Vorstegstock, 2679 m
Vrenelisgärtli, 2904 m
Wiggis, 2282 m
Wissgandstock, 2404 m
Zindlenspitz, 2097 m
Zuetribistock, 2644 m
Zwölfihörner
  Grosses, 2744 m
  Hinteres, 2741 m
  Vordere, I. II. III.

13
The Säntis Region

Altenalptürm
  2019 m
  2031 m
Altmann, 2436 m
Amboss, 1926 m
Bogartenfirst, 1811 m
Chreialpfirst, 2125 m
Fälenschafberg, 2103 m

Fälentürm
  2224 m
  2219 m
  2227 m
Fänerenspitz, 1506 m
Freiheit, 2140 m
Freiheittürme
  2107 m
  2110 m
Gamskopf, 1959 m
Gätterifirst, 2050–2095 m
Girenspitz, 2253 m
Gulmen, 1992 m
Hängeten, 2064–2211 m
Hoher Kasten, 1794 m
Hundstein, 2156 m
Hüser, 1951 m
Jöchli, 2335 m
Kamor, 1751 m
Kirchli, 1914 m
Kreuzberge
  I. 1884 m
  II. 1970 m
  III. 2020 m
  IV. 2059 m
  V. 2054 m
  VI. 2044 m
  VII. 2065 m
  VIII. 2056 m
Kronberg, 1663 m
Lütispitz, 1986 m
Marwees, 2055 m
Moor, 2344 m
Mutschen, 2121 m
Nadlenspitz, 2030 m
Neuenalpspitz, 1816 m
Öhrli, 2192 m
Roslenfirst, 2151 m
Rot Turm, 2002 m
Säntis, 2501 m
Schafbergturm, 2128 m
Schäfler, 1923 m
Scherenspitzen, 1926 m
Scherenturm, 1907 m
Schwarzkopf, 1948 m
Silberplatten, 2158 m
  Silberplattenköpfe, I–VI
Stauberenchanzlen, 1860 m
Stockberg, 1781 m
Stöllen
  1986 m
  1967 m
Stoss, 2110 m
Widderalpstöck
  1986 m
  2058 m
  2066 m
Wildhuser Schafberg, 2373 m

Wildhuser Schafberg-
  köpfe, 2311–2325 m

14
*Toggenburg and the
St Gallen Highlands*

Älplichopf, 2641 m
Alvier, 2343 m
Brisi, 2279 m
Chäserrugg, 2262 m
Chli Schibe, 2654 m
Chrummhorn, 2706 m
Chüemettler, 1703 m
Crap Mats, 2941 m
Drachenberg, 2605 m
Fanenstock, 2612 m
Federispitz, 1865 m
Felsberger Calanda, 2696 m
Flimserstein, 2694 m
Flügenspitz, 1703 m
Foostock, 2610 m
Frümsel, 2263 m
Fulfirst, 2383 m
Gamsberg, 2384 m
Gamserrugg, 2076 m
Gärtlichöpf, 2298 m
Gauschla, 2310 m
Gigerwaldspitz, 2291 m
Glaserhorn, 3128 m
Glattchamm, 2098 m
Goggeien [Schär], 1655 m
Gonzen, 1829 m
Graue Hörner
  Wildseehörner, 2690 m
  Lavtinahörner, 2767 m
  Schwarze Hörner, 2645 m
Gross Schibe, 2937 m
Gulmen, 1788 m
Haldensteiner Calanda, 2805 m
Hangsackgrat, 2580 m
Hinterrugg, 2306 m
Hochfinsler, 2421 m
Hochwart, 2671 m
Hüenerchopf, 2171 m
Kaminspitz, 1813 m
Laritschchopf, 2498 m
Leistchamm, 2101 m
Magerrain, 2524 m
Margelchopf, 2162 m
Mattstock, 1935 m
Morkopf, 2943 m
Muntaluna, 2421 m
Nägeliberg, 2163 m
Orglen, I–VI, 2720 m

Panärahörner
  3106 m
  3057 m
Plattenspitz, 2579 m
Pizalun, 1478 m
Piz Mirutta, 2605 m
Piz Sardona, 3055 m
Piz Sax, 2795 m
Piz Segnas, 3098 m
Pizol, 2844 m
Ringelspitz, 3247 m
Rosskirche, ohne Kote LK
Rotrüfner, 2462 m
Sächsmor, 2195 m
Sazmartinhorn, 2827 m
Schafgrat, 2763 m
Schären, 2171 m
Schibenstoll, 2234 m
Selun, 2204 m
  Silberspitz
Sennenstein, 1999 m
Sessagit [Turm], 1907 m
Sichelchamm, 2269 m
Simel, 2354 m
Speer, 1950 m
Spitzmeilen, 2502 m
Taminser Calanda, 2389 m
Trinserhorn, 3028 m
Tristelhorn, 3114 m
Tristencholben, 2159 m
Vättner Chopf, 2616 m
Wart, 2068 m
Wissmilen, 2483 m
Zanaihorn, 2821 m
Zinerspitz, 2508 m
Zuestollen, 2235 m
Zweierspitz, 1858 m

15
*Central Grisons
between Rhine and Inn*

Alperschellihorn, 3039 m
Älpliseehorn, 2725 m
Amperveilerhorn, 2802 m
Amselfluh, 2771 m
Aroser Rothorn, 2980 m
Aroser Weisshorn, 2653 m
Bärenhorn, 2929 m
Bocktenhorn, 3044 m
Bruschghorn, 3043 m
Bühlenhorn, 2807 m
Casanna, 2557 m
Cima Camadra, 3172 m
Cho d'Survetta, 2960 m

Corn Alv, 2980 m
Corn Suvretta, 3071 m
Corn da Tinizong, 3172 m
Crap Grisch, 2861 m
Crasta Mora, 2935 m
Cufercalhorn, 2799 m
Dreibündenstein, 2174 m
Erzhorn, 2923 m
Faltschonhorn, 3022 m
Fanellahorn, 3123 m
Flüela Schwarzhorn, 3146 m
Frunthorn, 3030 m
Furggeltihorn, 3043 m
Furkahorn, 2727 m
Gelbhorn, 3035 m
Glattwang, 2376 m
Grauhorn, 3260 m
Güferhorn, 3381 m
Guggernell, 2744 m
Günerhorn, 2849 m
Guralätschhorn, 2908 m
Hoch Ducan, 3063 m
   Klein Ducan, 3006 m
   Gletscher Ducan, 3019 m
Hochwang, 2532 m
Hohberghorn, 3004 m
Jakobshorn, 2590 m
Jatzhorn, 2681 m
Igls Dschimels
   2777 m
   2782 m
Kirchalphorn, 3039 m
Kistenstein, 2473 m
Krachenhorn, 2890 m
Kühalphorn, 3077 m
Küpfenfluh, 2658 m
La Bianca, 2993 m
La Löggia, 3079 m
La Piramida, 2963 m
Las Trais Fluors, 2954 m
Leidbachhorn, 2908 m
Lentahorn, 3227 m
Lenzerhorn, 2906 m
Lorenzhorn, 3044 m
Marscholhorn, 2962 m
Mattlishorn, 2460 m
Medergerfluh, 2674 m
Montalin, 2266 m
Paradieshörnli, 2963 m
Parpaner Rothorn, 2863 m
Parpaner Schwarzhorn, 2683 m
Parpaner Weisshorn, 2775 m
Piz d'Agnel, 3205 m
Piz Albana, 3099 m
Piz Alpettas, 2978 m
Piz Alpetta, 2863 m
Pizzas d'Anarosa, 3000 m
   2902 m

Piz Arblatsch, 3203 m
Piz Arpschella, 3032 m
Piz Ault, 3121 m
Piz digl Barba Peder, 2746 m
Piz Bardella, 2899 m
Piz Barscheinz, 2617 m
Piz Bever, 3230 m
Piz Beverin, 2997 m
Piz Bial, 3061 m
Piz Blaisun, 3200 m
Piz Blas, 3018 m
Piz Bleisch Marscha, 3128 m
Piz Borel, 2952 m
Piz Cagniel, 2970 m
Piz Calandari, 2555 m
Piz Calderas, 3397 m
Piz de Canal, 2846 m
Piz Caschleglia, 2935 m
Piz Cavel, 2945 m
Piz Cavradi, 2612 m
Piz Champagnung, 2825 m
Piz Chembels, 2981 m
Piz Clüna, 3102 m
Piz dallas Coluonnas, 2960 m
Piz Coroi, 2785 m
Piz Corviglia, 3057 m
Piz Crealetsch, 2950 m
Piz Cristallina, 3128 m
Piz da Cucarnegl, 3051 m
Piz Cugnets, 2739 m
Piz Curvèr, 2971 m
   Curvèr Pintg da Neaza, 2720 m
   Curvèr Pintg da
   Taspegn, 2730 m
Piz Danis, 2496 m
Piz Ela, 3180 m
Piz d'Emmat dadaint, 2927 m
   Piz d'Emmat dadora, 2851 m
Piz d'Err, 3378 m
Piz Fess, 2880 m
Piz Fòrbesch, 3261 m
Piz Forun, 3052 m
Piz Gaglianera, 3121 m
Piz Gannaretsch, 3039 m
Piz Git, 2968 m
Piz Gren, 2890 m
Piz Grevasalvas, 2932 m
Piz Grialetsch, 3131 m
Piz Griatschouls, 2972 m
Piz Grisch, 3098 m
Piz Güda, 2845 m
Pizza dil Gurschus
   2753 m
   2844 m
   2880 m
Piz Julier, 3380 m
Piz Kesch, 3417 m
   Aguoglia dal Kesch, 3386 m

Piz Lai Blau, 2961 m
Piz Lavinèr, 3137 m
Piz Lunghin, 2780 m
Piz Máler, 2790 m
Piz Marsch, 3120 m
Piz Martegnas, 2670 m
Piz Materdell, 2966 m
Piz Medel, 3210 m
Piz Mitgel, 3158 m
Pizzo Moèsola, 2966 m
Piz Mulix, 2887 m
Piz Mundaun, 2064 m
Piz Muraun, 2897 m
Piz Murterchömbel, 2996 m
Piz Muschaneras, 2604 m
Piz Müsella, 2896 m
Piz Nadéls, 2788 m
Piz Nair, 3057 m
Piz Neir, 2909 m
Piz Ot, 3246 m
Piz Padella, 2884 m
Piz Palpuogna, 2733 m
Piz Paradis, 2883 m
Piz Picuogl, 3333 m
Piz Platta Roggia, 2955 m
Piz Porchabella, 3079 m
Piz Puntota, 3019 m
Piz Radönt, 3065 m
   Radünerköpfe
Piz dal Ras, 3024 m
Piz Ravetsch, 3006 m
Piz Ravigliel, 2987 m
Piz Regina, 2532 m
Piz Rentiert, 2614 m
Piz Riein, 2752 m
Piz Rondadura, 3015 m
Piz Salteras, 3110 m
Piz Saluver, 3159 m
Piz Santeri, 2880 m
Piz Sarsura, 3177 m
   Sarsuret, 3126 m
   Piz Sarsura Pitschen, 3133 m
Piz dal Sasc, 2720 m
Piz Scalottas, 2324 m
Piz Scharboden, 3122 m
Piz Schlattein, 3004 m
Piz Seranastga, 2874 m
Piz Serengia, 2986 m
Piz Sezner, 2309 m
Piz Signina, 2848 m
Piz Spadlatscha, 2871 m
Piz Spegnas, 2620 m
Piz Spinas, 2865 m
Piz Surgonda, 3197 m
Piz Suvretta, 3144 m
Piz Starlera, 2711 m
Piz Stavelatsch, 2753 m
Piz Tarantschun, 2768 m

Piz Terri, 3149 m
Piz Tgietschen, 2857 m
Piz Titschal, 2548 m
Piz Toissa, 2656 m
Piz Tomül, 2946 m
Piz Traunterovas, 3150 m
Piz la Tschera, 2627 m
Piz Üertsch, 3267 m
Piz Uffiern, 3151 m
Piz Uffiern, 3013 m
Piz d'Uglix, 2967 m
Piz d'Urezza, 2906 m
Piz Vadret, 3229 m
   Piz Vadret Pitschen, 3106 m
Piz Valdraus, 3096 m
Piz Vallatscha, 3109 m
Piz Valletta, 2933 m
Piz Val Lunga, 3078 m
Piz Val Müra, 3162 m
Piz Val Nova, 3051 m
Piz Vatgira, 2982 m
Piz Vial, 3168 m
Piz Viluoch, 3042 m
Piz Viroula, 3064 m
Piz de Vrin, 2546 m
Piz Zavretta, 3043 m
Präzer Höhe, 2119 m
Rheinquellhorn, 3200 m
Rheinwaldhorn, 3402 m
Roccabella, 2731 m
Salahorn, 2984 m
Scalettahorn, 3068 m
Schwarzhorn, 3114 m
Schwarzhorn, 3025 m
Schwarzhorn, 2944 m
Schiahorn, 2709 m
Scopï, 3198 m
Sentishorn, 2827 m
Stätzerhorn, 2574 m
Steilerhorn, 2980 m
Teischerhorn, 2688 m
Teurihorn, 2973 m
Tgiern de Vanescha, 2471 m
Tiejerfluh, 2781 m
Tomülgrat, 2738 m
Torrone di Gar zora, 3017 m
Tschima da Flix, 3316 m
Tschima da Tisch, 2871 m
Valbellahorn, 2764 m
Valserhorn, 2885 m
Vogelberg, 3218 m
Wannenspitz, 2444 m
Weissfluh, 2843 m
Weisshorn, 2988 m
Wuosthorn, 2814 m
Zapporthorn, 3151 m
Zervreilerhorn, 2898 m

16

Rätikon, Silvretta, Samnaun

Älpeltispitz, 2685 m
Augstenberg, 3230 m
Bürkelkopf, 3033 m
Canardhorn, 2607 m
Dreiländerspitz, 3197 m
Drusenfluh, 2827 m
Drusentürme
   Grosser, 2830 m
   Kleiner, 2754 m
Eckhorn, 3147 m
Eisentälispitz, 2873 m
Falknis, 2562 m
Fergenhorn
   Grosses, 2680 m
   Kleines
   Fergenkegel, 2844 m
Flimspitze, 2928 m
Fluchthorn
   3398 m
   3397 m
   3146 m
Flüela Weisshorn, 3085 m
Gemsspitz, 3107 m
Gleckhorn, 2237 m
Gorihorn, 2986 m
Grauspitz, 2599 m
Grübelekopf, 2893 m
Gross Litzner, 3109 m
Hornspitz, 2536 m
Jamspitze
   Vordere, 3176 m
   Hintere, 3156 m
Kessispitz, 2833 m
Kessler, 2836 m
Kirchlispitzen, 2552 m
Kreuz, 2195 m
Krone, 3186 m
Madrisahorn, 2826 m
Muttler, 3294 m
Naafkopf, 2570 m
Paulinerkopf, 2863 m
Pischahorn, 2979 m
Piz d'Antschatscha, 2978 m
Piz Arina, 2828 m
Piz Buin grand, 3312 m
   Piz Buin pitschen, 3250 m
Piz Chamins, 2927 m
Piz Champatsch, 2969 m
Piz Champatsch, 2919 m
Piz Chapisum, 2931 m
Piz da las Clavigliadas, 2984 m
Piz Cotschen, 3030 m
Piz Davo Lais, 3026 m
Piz Faschalba, 3047 m

Piz Fless, 3020 m
Piz Fliana, 3281 m
Piz Jeramias, 3087 m
Piz Larain, 3009 m
Piz Lavèr, 2984 m
Piz Linard, 3410 m
Piz Malmurainza, 3038 m
Piz Mezdi, 2918 m
Piz Minschun, 3068 m
Piz Mottana, 2927 m
Piz Mundin, 3120 m
   Aguoglia dal Mundin
Piz Murtera, 3044 m
Piz Roz, 3097 m
Piz Sagliains, 3101 m
Piz Soèr, 2916 m
Piz Spadla, 2912 m
Piz Tasna, 3172 m
Piz Tiatscha, 3051 m
Piz Tuoi, 3084 m
Piz Urschai, 3097 m
Piz Valtorta, 2975 m
Piz Zadrell, 3104 m
Plattenhörner
   3216 m
   3220 m
   3101 m
   3200 m
Plattenspitzen, 2883 m
   Garneraturm
Rätschenfluh, 2703 m
Rosstälispitz, 2929 m
Rotbühlspitz, 2852 m
Rotfluh, 3166 m
Sassauna, 2307 m
Scheienfluh, 2624 m
   Scheienzahn
Schesaplana, 2964 m
Schiltfluh, 2887 m
Schollberg, 2570 m
Seehorn
   Grosses, 3121 m
   Kleines, 3031 m
Seeschyen, 2772 m
Signalhorn, 3207 m
Silvrettahorn, 3244 m
Sulerspitz, 3034 m
Sulzfluh, 2817 m
Stammerspitz, 3254 m
Tschingel, 2541 m
Unghührhörner
   2879 m
   2994 m
   2992 m
Vilan, 2375 m

17

Avers, Splügen, Misox, Calanca

Alta Burrasca, 2652 m
Cima di Barna, 2862 m
Cima di Bedoletta, 2626 m
Cima da Cävi, 2846 m
Cima dei Cogn, 3062 m
Cima di Colle Scengio, 2421 m
Cima di Cugn, 2237 m
Cima di Gaigèla, 2805 m
Cima di Lago, 3083 m
Cima di Lugezzasca, 2716 m
Cima d'Orzo, 2706 m
Cima di Pian Guarnei, 3015 m
Cima dei Rossi, 2726 m
Cima della Sovranna, 3016 m
Cima dello Stagno, 2382 m
Cima di Val Loga, 3004 m
Cima di Verchenca, 2858 m
Cimalmotta, 2835 m
Einshorn, 2943 m
Fil di Dragiva, 2787 m
Fil di Gordasc, 2095 m
Fil di Remia, 2914 m
Fil Rosso, 3160 m
Gletscherhorn, 3107 m
Guggernüll, 2886 m
Guglie d'Altare, 3172 m
Hüreli, 2854 m
Il Pizzaccio, 2588 m
Jupperhorn, 3155 m
Marmontana, 2190 m
Mazzaspitz, 3164 m
Monte Balniscio, 2851 m
Mottone, 2739 m
Mottone, 2692 m
Pan di Zucchero, 2601 m
Piz Alv, 2854 m
Pizzo d'Arbeòla, 2600 m
Pizzo Ardion, 2506 m
Pizzo Bianco, 3036 m
Piz Bles, 3044 m
Piz Cam, 2634 m
Pizzo Campanile, 2556 m
Pizzo di Campedello, 2724 m
Pizzo di Campel, 2376 m
Pizzo Cavriola, 2873 m
Pizzo Corbet, 3025 m
P. di Cressim, 2575 m
Piz del Crot, 2845 m
Pizzo di Curciusa, 2871 m
Piz Duan, 3130 m
Pizzo Ferrè, 3103 m
Piz Forcellina, 2936 m
Pizzo della Forcola, 2620 m
Pizzo Galleggione, 3107 m

Piz Grisch, 3060 m
Pizzo di Groven, 2693 m
Piz Lagrev, 3164 m
Piz Lizun, 2518 m
Pizzo Lumbreda, 2982 m
Piz Mäder, 3001 m
Pizzo Martello, 2459 m
Piz la Mazza, 2815 m
Piz dal Märc, 2909 m
Pizzo della Molera, 2602 m
Pizzo Montagna, 2661 m
Pizzo Mottun, 2853 m
Pizzo Muccia, 2956 m
Piz Muttala, 2960 m
Pizzo Padion, 2631 m
Pizzo Paglia, 2593 m
Pizzo della Palù, 3172 m
Pizzo Papalin, 2714 m
P. di Pianascio, 2827 m
Pizzo Pian Grande, 2689 m
Pizzi dei Piani, 3148 m
Pizzo di Piodella, 2396 m
Piz Piot, 3053 m
Piz Platta, 3392 m
Piz Polaschin, 3013 m
Pizzo Pombi, 2967 m
Piz Por, 3028 m
Pizzo Rosso, 3053 m
Pizzo Rotondo, 2829 m
Piz Scalotta, 2991 m
Pizzo di Settacio, 2460 m
Pizzo di Settagiolo di
   dentro, 2565 m
Piz Settember, 2727 m
Pizzo Spadolazzo, 2720 m
Pizzo di Stabiuch, 2177 m
P. delle Streghe, 2911 m
Pizzo Tambo, 3279 m
Pizzo Termine, 2902 m
Piz Timun, 3208 m
Pizzo di Trescolmen, 2581 m
Piz Turba, 3018 m
Pizzo del Torto, 2723 m
Piz Ursaregls, 2837 m
Pizzo Uccello, 2719 m
Pizzo Vignone, 2859 m
Pizzo Zoccone, 3092 m
Poncione del Freccione, 3202 m
Poncione della Parete, 2984 m
Punta Levis, 2690 m
Sass Castell, 2515 m
Sass Mogn, 2440 m
Sasso della Guardia, 2092 m
Schiahorn [Avers], 2636 m
Schwarzhörner
   Äussere, 2890 m
   Mittler, 2837 m
   Inner, 2984 m

Schwarzseehorn, 2769 m
Surettahorn, 3027 m
Tälihorn, 3164 m
Tempahorn, 2619 m
Toresella, 2246 m
Torrente Alto, 2950 m
Tscheischhorn, 3019 m
Wängahorn, 2848 m
Weissberg
   Äusser, 3052 m
   Mittler, 2981 m
   Inner, 3002 m

18
*Southern Mountains of the Bergell
Passo Muretto to Castasegna*

Ago di Sciora, 3205 m
Castel, 2924 m
Cima della Bondasca, 3267 m
Cima di Cantone, 3354 m
Cima di Castello, 3392 m
Cime del Largo
   Punta Centrale, 3159 m
   Punta Est, 3188 m
   Punta Occidentale, 3136 m
Cima di Murtaira, 2857 m
Cima di Rosso, 3366 m
Cima di Spluga, 3046 m
Cima delle Teggiola, 2600 m
Cima di Val Bona, 3033 m
Cima di Vazzeda, 3301 m
Dente del Lupo, 2172 m
Ferro Occidentale, 3276 m
Ferro Orientale, 3199 m
Il Gallo, 2774 m
La Vergine, 2600 m
Lo Scalino, 3164 m
Monte del Forno, 3214 m
Monte Rosso, 3088 m
Monte Sissone, 3330 m
Piz Bacone, 3243 m
Piz Badile, 3308 m
Piz Badilet, 3171 m
Piz Balzetto, 2869 m
Piz Cacciabella Sud, 2900 m
   Piz Cacciabella Nord, 2980 m
Piz Casnile, 3189 m
Piz Cengalo, 3370 m
Piz Eravedar, 2934 m
Piz Frachiccio, 2905 m
Pizzi Gemelli
   3262 m
   3223 m
Piz Grand, 2459 m

Piz Murtaira, 2775 m
Piz dal Päl, 2618 m
Pizzo dei Rossi, 3026 m
Piz Salecina, 2599 m
Piz Spazzacaldera, 2487 m
   Fiamma
   Dente
Piz Torrone Orientale, 3333 m
   Piz Torrone Centrale,
   3290 m
   Piz Torrone Centrale
   ovest, 3270 m
   Piz Torrone Occiden-
   tale, 3349 m
   Ago del Torrone, 3233 m
Piz Trubinasca, 2918 m
Piz Val della Neve, 2600 m
Pizzi dei Vanni
   P. 2773 m
   P. 2734 m
Pizzo Zocca, 3174 m
Punta dell'Albigna, 2824 m
Punta Est dei Pizzi Centrali
   del Ferro, 3289 m
Punta Pioda di Sciora, 3238 m
Punta Rasica, 3305 m
Punta Sertori, 3195 m
Punta di Trubinasca, 2996 m
Sciora Dadent, 3275 m
Sciora Dafora, 3169 m
Scioretta, 3046 m
Torrione del Ferro, 3234 m

19
*Bernina group
Passo Muretto to Bernina Pass*

Bellavista
   3922 m
   3892 m
   3893 m
   3804 m
Cima Sondrio, 3542 m
Cima di Vartegna, 2732 m
Corno di Campascio, 2808 m
Corno dei Marci, 2805 m
Crast'Agüzza, 3869 m
Crasta dal Lej-Sgrischus,
   3303 m
Furtschellas, 2932 m
Il Chapütschin, 3386 m
Ils Dschimels
   3500 m
   3497 m
La Muongia, 3415 m

La Sella
   3584 m
   3564 m
Monte dell'Oro, 3154 m
Munt d'Arlas, 3127 m
Munt Pers, 3207 m
Piz dals Aguagliouls, 3118 m
Piz dal lej Alv, 3197 m
Piz Alv, 3995 m
Piz Argient, 3942 m
Piz d'Arlas
   3357 m
   3467 m
Piz Bernina, 4049 m
Piz Boval, 3353 m
Piz Cambrena, 3603 m
Pizzo Canciano, 3103 m
Pizzo Canciano, 2436 m
Piz Caral, 3422 m
Piz Chalchagn, 3158 m
Pizzo Combolo, 2900 m
Piz Corvatsch, 3451 m
Piz Fedoz, 3190 m
Piz Fora, 3363 m
Piz da la Fuorcl'ota, 3382 m
Piz Glüschaint, 3593 m
Piz Güz, 3080 m
Piz Led, 3087 m
Pizzo Malgina, 2877 m
Piz Mandra, 3091 m
Piz da la Margna, 3158 m
Piz Mezdi, 2992 m
Piz Misaun, 3248 m
Piz Morteratsch, 3751 m
Piz Muretto, 3103 m
Piz da l'Ova Cotschna, 2716 m
Piz Palü
   3905 m
   3882 m
   3823 m
Piz Prievlus, 3610 m
Piz Rosatsch, 3123 m
Piz Roseg, 3920 m
Piz Salatschina, 2824 m
Piz San Gian, 3124 m
Pizzo Sareggio, 2779 m
Piz Scerscen, 3971 m
Piz Sella, 3511 m
Piz Surlej, 3188 m
Piz da Staz, 2847 m
Piz Tremoggia, 3441 m
Piz Trovat, 3146 m
Piz Tschierva, 3545 m
Piz Umur, 3252 m
Pizzo Varuna, 3452 m
Piz Zupò, 3995 m
Sassalmason, 3031 m

20
*Central and lower
Engadine
south of the Inn*

Banderola, 2795 m
Cima di Cárdan, 2904 m
Cima delle Gandi Rossi, 2831 m
Cima di Rüggiol, 2986 m
Cima di Saoseo, 3265 m
Cima del Serraglio, 2684 m
Corno di Campo, 3232 m
Corno di Dosté, 3232 m
Corno Mürisciola, 2819 m
Crasta Burdun, 3133 m
Cuclèr da Jon dad Onsch, 2775 m
Griankopf, 2892 m
Las Suors
   3008 m
   2978 m
Monte Forcola, 2906 m
Munt Cotschen, 3103 m
Munt Gravatscha, 2752 m
Muntpitschen, 3162 m
Piz dell'Acqua, 3118 m
Piz Ajüz, 2788 m
Piz Ajüz, 2754 m
Piz Albris, 3165 m
Piz Alv, 2974 m
Piz d'Arpiglias, 3027 m
Piz d'Astras, 2980 m
Piz Campasc, 2598 m
Piz Chaschanella, 2929 m
Piz Chaschauna, 3070 m
Piz Chatscheders, 2985 m
Piz Chazfora, 3006 m
Piz Clemgia, 3042 m
Piz Clüx, 3128 m
Piz Confine, 2905 m
Piz Cristannes, 3092 m
Piz Curtinatsch, 2863 m
Piz Daint, 2968 m
Piz dal Diavel, 3062 m
Piz Dora, 2951 m
Piz Dössaradond, 2906 m
Piz d'Esan, 3127 m
Piz Fier, 3058 m
Piz Foraz, 3092 m
Piz Ftur, 3022 m
Piz dal Fuorn, 2908 m
Piz Giarsinom, 2665 m
Piz d'Immez, 3026 m
Piz Ivraina, 2886 m
Piz Lad, 2881 m
Piz Lad, 2784 m
Piz Lagalb, 2959 m
Piz Languard, 3261 m

Piz Laschadurella, 3005 m
Piz Lavetscha, 2790 m
Piz Lavirun, 3052 m
Piz dals Lejs, 3041 m
Piz Lischana, 3105 m
Piz Macun, 2888 m
Piz Madlain, 3098 m
Piz Magliavachas, 3044 m
Piz Mezdì, 2927 m
Piz Mezdì, 2726 m
Piz Mezzaun, 2962 m
Piz Mingèr, 3081 m
Piz Minor, 3049 m
Piz Mon Ata, 2937 m
Piz Muragl, 3157 m
Piz Murtarous, 2928 m
Piz Murtaröl, 3180 m
Piz Murtèr, 2836 m

Piz Murters, 3012 m
Piz Murters, 2969 m
Piz Murtiröl, 2660 m
Piz Nair, 3009 m
Piz Nair, 2951 m
Piz Nuna, 3123 m
    Cuclèr da Nuna
Piz Pala Gronda, 3002 m
Piz Paradisino, 3302 m
Piz Pischa, 3138 m
Piz Pisoc, 3173 m
Piz Plattas, 3052 m
Piz Plavna Dadaint, 3166 m
Piz Plavna Dadora, 2981 m
Piz Plazer, 3004 m
Piz Praveder, 2763 m
Piz Prüna, 3158 m
Piz Quattervals, 3154 m

Piz Rims, 2772 m
Piz Russenna, 2802 m
Piz Sagliant, 2826 m
Pizzo Saliente, 3043 m
Piz Sampuoir, 3023 m
Piz San Jon, 3093 m
Piz S-chalambert Dadora, 2678 m
Piz S-chalambert Dadaint,
    3029 m
Piz Schumbraida, 3124 m
Pizzo di Sena, 3074 m
Piz Serra, 3093 m
Piz Sesvenna, 3204 m
Piz Sursassa, 2968 m
Piz Starlex, 3066 m
Piz la Stretta, 3104 m
Piz Tantermozza, 2983 m
Piz Tavrü, 3167 m

Piz Tea Fondada, 3144 m
Piz del Teo, 3049 m
Piz Terza, 2910 m
Piz Terza, 2681 m
Pizzo Trevisina, 2832 m
Piz Triazza, 3041 m
Piz Trupchum, 2941 m
Piz Turettas, 2957 m
Piz Umbrail, 3031 m
Piz Utèr, 2967 m
Piz Vadret, 3199 m
Piz Vallatscha, 3021 m
Piz Valnera, 3160 m
Piz Vaüglia, 2973 m
Piz Zuort, 3118 m
Punta Casana, 3007 m
Punta di Rims, 2946 m
Sassalbo, 2841 m

Technical Information on the Photographs

For almost all the photographs in this book, I used two Leica type M2 cameras and the following lenses:

 35 mm Leitz Summilux f 1.4
 35 mm Leitz Summaron f 3.5
 85 mm Canon Lens f 1.8
 90 mm Leitz Elmar f 4
200 mm Leitz Telyt f 4

Some of the photographs (details) of animals and landscapes were obtained with the Pentax Single Lens Reflex Camera and a Russian Mirror Telephoto f 8, 500 mm lens.

The Leica has the advantage in the mountains of being compact and of robust construction. I have had this camera with me even on the most difficult ascents, invariably without the ever-ready case which I find an impediment. By using a short neck strap, the camera is always ready for taking pictures in awkward places.

For all photographs, provided the light is adequate, I have always used the very fine-grain Kodak Panatomic-X film (17 DIN). For pictures in poor light (inside the hut, or in twilight) I have used Kodak Tri-X film (25 DIN).

Colour material: Ektachrome and Kodachrome.

Filter: Yellow-green filter for black and white landscapes.

Acknowledgements

My sincere thanks to all mountain companions who have accompanied me on many expeditions; it would have been quite impossible to write this book without them. To Paul Etter, mountain guide from Walenstadt, I am indebted for some of the most difficult ascents. The guide René Arnold from Zermatt, together with Paul Etter, were my companions on extensive tours in the Valais. Walter Belina, guide from Chur, was the rope expert on the Badile face, Ernst Brülisauer, who has compiled the index to the peaks, has been my companion on the rope over a period of twenty years.

My thanks must also be extended to the large company of those comrades whose love of mountains turned out fatally for them. Dr Ricco Bianchi, who wrote the contributions on the natural life of the Alps, fell to his death on the Tinzenhorn a few months after completing this work. The writings of Ricco Bianchi are the memorial to a dedicated mountain naturalist and explorer.

Herbert Maeder

The colour photographs of the flowers are by Dr Ricco Bianchi; the photograph used for the outer cover is the work of Philipp Giegel of the Swiss National Tourist Office. The contribution "On Admiring the Alps" by Konrad Gessner has been taken from the book *Die Entstehung der Alpen* and reproduced with the kind permission of the publishers, Verlag Huber & Co. AG, Frauenfeld 1934. The work *The Mountains of Switzerland* has been greatly assisted by the willing co-operation of the Swiss National Tourist Office.